Much Wenlock's
Limestone Quarries

Much Wenlock's Limestone Quarries

Glyn Williams

Ellingham Press

First published in 1997

Revised and reprinted by Ellingham Press 2014

ISBN 978-0-9926031-5-1

British Library Cataloguing in Publication Data
A catalogue record is available for this book from the British Library

Ellingham Press, 43 High Street, Much Wenlock, Shropshire TF13 6AD
www.ellinghampress.co.uk

Cover by Aardvark Illustration & Design
www.aardvarkid.com

Typesetting by ISB Typesetting, Sheffield
www.sheffieldtypesetting.co.uk

Printed in UK by Tyson Press

Contents

Preface

The history of quarrying around Much Wenlock is very scantily documented. In this book therefore, an attempt has been made to examine and record the amount of limestone workings that has taken place within the limited area of some three miles either side of Much Wenlock, chiefly on the north-south axis; to date as near as possible (the main period covered is in fact scarcely more than 280 years) the origin, decline and, in some cases, the revival of individual quarries and limeworks, to illustrate and describe the typical enterprises; to examine briefly the geology, properties and industrial uses of the limestone, together with a description of the various modes and methods of extraction and preparation that were used.

I published two previous books in 1990 and 1997, entitled *The Wenlock Limestone Industry: an historical note* and this is an update of those. In the intervening time further important documentary evidence came to light and more oral evidence was obtained which justified the rewriting. Although many references and sources have been firmed up, there are some whose exact whereabouts escape me.

Glyn Williams
Much Wenlock 2014

Introduction

Limestone has been produced in Wenlock and its environs for probably the last eight or nine centuries (the Priory ruins and Holy Trinity Church have local limestone in their fabric). Archaeologists now believe that some of the stone used to build the Roman city of Wroxeter (Uriconium) also came from Wenlock quarries. However, the first evidence of quarrying was in the years 1399–1400 when quantities of 'building lyme' were supplied to Caus Castle.[1] By 1586 Wenlock had become known for its lime[2] and in 1594 sixteen loads of stone were sent to repair Shrewsbury School.[3] However, it was not until much later, in fact early in the eighteenth century, that there emerges any detailed evidence of quarrying taking place on a commercial basis. This was at Hilltop, Easthope; on Westwood Common; off Blakeway Hollow; on Tomlinson's Hills and on Gleedon Hill.

In the years 1789–90 there were 13 lime-burners on the Wynnstay Estate (the present Gaskell Estate) who collectively produced 3503 wagonloads of lime and limestone.[4]

It was, however, only within the last 200 hundred years or so that observers and chroniclers noted the growing importance of the Wenlock limestone industry.

Writing in 1800, Thomas Telford suggested that a canal be built from the River Severn to Wenlock, Cleobury Mortimer, Church Stretton and Ludlow for the carriage, amongst other things, of limestone.[5]

In 1824 the *Shropshire Gazetteer* noted that Wenlock, with 481 houses and a population of 2,200, was famous for its limestone quarries, whilst Murchison wrote in 1838, in his now famous geological thesis, *The Silurian System* '…there are many quarries on the summit and south slopes of Wenlock Edge and on both sides of the road which transverses the ridge.'

In 1831 it is recorded that there were 130 men employed in the quarries,[6] who constituted 17% of the town's workforce.[7]

In the period 1851–2, over 36,000 tons of limestone were being transported down the Farley road and some 2,000 tons of lime were being produced.[8]

In 1861 the Wenlock Council petitioned in favour of the Railway Bill which was being promoted to allow a railway to be built to Much Wenlock: 'It considered a good trade would be had for raw material carriage...and in the raising of limestone for fluxing purposes in the iron districts.'[9] In fact there was opposition to the proposed railway by the newly opened Severn Valley Railway. It was argued 'that the gradients were too great (at one point a massive 1 in 43) the curves too abrupt and the traffic was insufficient'. However, John Anstice of the Madeley Wood Company, together with other businessmen and landowners, including Lord Wenlock, the agent for Lord Forester, and George Benson of Lutwyche Hall, supporting the Bill said, 'Madeley sent coal and bricks to Wenlock and that upwards of 40,000 tons of limestone per annum was being sent to the ironworks.'[10]

The year 1862 saw Wenlock linked by rail to the East Shropshire coalfield and the Black Country, but only by the Severn valley route via Shrewsbury or Kidderminster, a track having been laid from Buildwas.[11] This was later extended, first to Presthope in 1864 and later to Marshbrook Junction in 1867, thus making limestone south of the town more readily accessible. In 1865 John Fowler, railway engineer, in his report to the directors of the Wenlock Railway Company, wrote: 'During the past six months the portion of this line (Wenlock to Presthope) has been opened for mineral traffic...and a large traffic in limestone has been carried which is steadily increasing.'[12]

By 1868 the business of Wenlock in lime and limestone had exceeded 120,000 tons.[13]

John Randall in his *Tourist's Guide to Wenlock* (published in 1875) wrote of the industry 'passing rude rocks, where hammers, crowbars and blasting powder are at work procuring flux for the iron districts'.

However, between the latter half of the nineteenth century (save for the First World War period) and the Second World War, there was a general decline in the limestone trade. The official Wenlock guide book of 1933 states 'this industry (limestone) has experienced lean years, but is rapidly passing into a more prosperous period'. In fact, this prosperous period did not materialise until the outbreak of the Second World War, when demand for ground limestone for soil fertilisation regenerated the industry. In the post-war years the industry was relatively buoyant and, save for a few years when recessional factors made trading difficult, quite prosperous.

Apart from a fundamental alteration of the immediate landscape, the limestone industry has had an advantageous, social and economic, influence on the town. This has ranged from the original provision of building stone for the construction of local buildings to bringing a modicum of wealth and prosperity to sections of the community. In 1979 approximately 100 people, some 15% of the local workforce, were employed, directly or otherwise, in the industry.[14]

Introduction

In small measure the limestone has been an inspiration for place names, for example, Quarry Piece Field (off Blakeway Lane), Kiln Leasow (off Stretton Road), Rock Field (above Sytche Coppice) and the Rock House Inn and the Limeman's Arms. In greater measure perhaps, limestone quarrying had an influence on the coming of the railway to Much Wenlock, with (at that time) all its attendant advantages. However, with the demise of the railway, all quarry products were despatched by road, totalling about one million tonnes per annum, the bulk of which was used for aggregates, in various forms, in the construction industry, around another 10% was used in concrete based products, 8% for agricultural lime and a minute proportion for fluxing purposes and building stone.[15] The maximum radius of distribution was around 60 miles, the chief criterion being when the cost of transportation equated with that of production.[16]

Before identifying and tracing the history of individual quarries, it would be useful first to examine briefly the geology of the area, the properties of the limestone and the various ways it has been used, to establish why this particular rock has been so much in demand over the years.

References and Sources

1   D.C. Cox et al., *The Victoria History of the Counties of England: A History of Shropshire*, vol. X (Oxford, OUP, 1998)
2   W. Camden, *Britannia*, vol. I (1588)
3   *Victoria County History*
4   Wynnstay box, National Library of Wales
5   J. Plymley, *General View of the Agriculture of Shropshire* (London, Sherwood, Neely & Jones, 1803)
6   1831 Census
7   Cox, op. cit.
8   Summers/Adney/Brookes, 'Railway Survey', Wenlock Archives
9   Wenlock Council Minute Book, 1875
10 J. Randall, *Tourist's Guide to Wenlock* (Madeley, Lawley & Wenlock, Randall, 1875)
11 Randall
12 Microfilm 113, Shrewsbury Local Studies Library
13 Wenlock Railway Company papers, PRO Kew
14 *Kelly's Directory*, 1868
15 SCC, 'Mineral Extraction on Wenlock Edge', 1979
16 V. Russell, manager, Shadwell Quarry, Steetley Construction Ltd, 1989

Geology

The limestone which comprises the volume of Wenlock Edge and to which the town has given its name (Wenlock Series of Silurian Limestone) was laid down some 400 million years ago.

Silurian rocks of this area (Silurian is taken from the name 'Silures', an ancient tribe associated with Shropshire and the Welsh borderland) belong to the sedimentary, shelly facies (shallow water beds) type of rock and when formed, the climate was tropical, much akin to the Caribbean area of today. Geologically, Silurian rocks are old, only being preceded by the Cambrian and Ordovician rock systems.

At the beginning of the Silurian period, the Wenlock area seems to have formed part of the western shore which bordered on to a sea stretching across northern England and the northern half of Wales in a north-east to south-west direction. As time went on, the land mass began to sink and the sea gradually extended until it covered not only the Wenlock district but nearly the whole of southern and central England and Wales. On the bed of this sea was laid down a series of deposits which later hardened into rocks now known as the Wenlock and Ludlow Series of Silurian Limestone, the whole process taking some 30 million years.[1]

The limestone, by sedimentary standards, is a relatively hard, resistant rock, highly fossiliferous and lying between two much softer rocks, the Wenlock shales to the north-west and the Ludlow shales to the south-east.

Under the forces of erosion – wind, rain, sun and frost – these softer rocks have been worn down, especially where they outcrop, leaving the limestone which has resisted erosion standing out above the surrounding countryside in the form of an escarpment about 100 metres high and behind which is a gentle slope (approximately 15 degrees to the horizontal plane) at the angle of the dip of the limestone beds.

Wenlock limestone is generally whitish to bluish-grey in colour and is found in calcareous beds of about 35 metres in thickness. The transition from Wenlock shales (which underlie the limestone) to Wenlock limestone is very gradual. This is evident by the sandy,

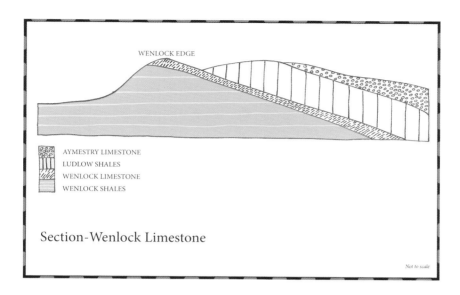

WENLOCK EDGE

AYMESTRY LIMESTONE
LUDLOW SHALES
WENLOCK LIMESTONE
WENLOCK SHALES

Section-Wenlock Limestone

Not to scale

light brown colour and composition of the limestone at the base of the beds, plus the flaky-flaggy nature of the rock in the lower stratum.

The capping of the rock is invariably a three-to-five metre band of crinoidal limestone. This is the solidified layer of crinoid lilies (a marine animal and not a plant) which formed the final stratifications of the Wenlock limestone.

The limestone is rich in the fossilised remains of many kinds of sea creatures, such as coral facies, crinoids, brachiopods (shellfish), stromatoporoids (solidified sponge-like coral), cephalopods (flat, spiral or sometimes squid-like shellfish) together with a good development of lingula (inarticula brachiopods).[2]

A notable feature of Wenlock limestone is the occurrence of reef-knolls, known locally as 'ballstone'. Ballstone may be found in any sequence, save possibly for the top crindoidal band. It is commonest, however, towards the bottom of the beds. Ballstones are made largely from skeletons of reef-forming organisms, particularly corals and stromatoporoids, and are set in a matrix of rock. These knolls are essentially unstratified. Generally the stratified limestone stops abruptly when it abuts against the ballstone, except near the top of the masses where it often curves over it.

Ballstone masses have been known to attain diameters of 27 metres.[3] They are to be found over most of the area under consideration, especially to the north (for instance Standhill and Bradley Quarries are principally reef-knolls) but appear to thin out rapidly

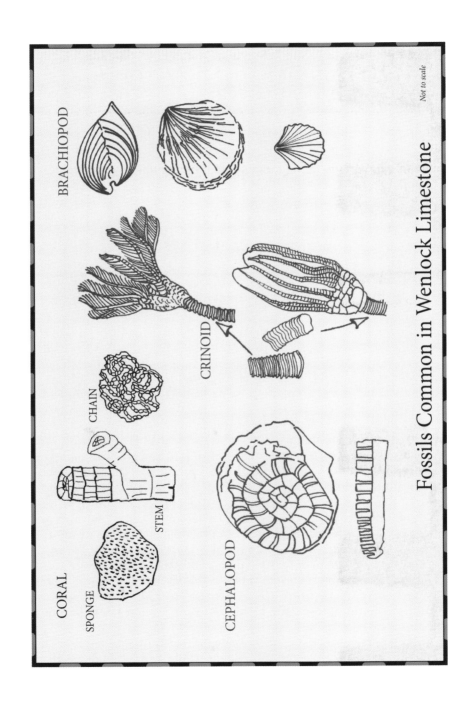

Fossils Common in Wenlock Limestone

Bedded limestone can be seen to the left in this section and unstratified ballstone to the right.

The top band of this quarry face is chiefly crinoidal limestone.

and diminish in size south of Presthope, although good examples can be seen in Lilleshall Quarry. Ballstones are rich in calcium carbonate and were much sought after, especially by early quarriers, for their fluxing qualities and for conversion to calcium oxide.

References and Sources

1   Borough of Wenlock official guide, 1955
2   Geological Survey (Shrewsbury District), 1938
3   D.C. Greig et al., *Memoirs of the Geological Survey of Great Britain* (London, HMSO, 1968)

The Properties of Wenlock Limestone

Limestone is partly organic, being composed of the fossilised remains of coral and other marine life, and partly, and to a somewhat lesser extent, a mixture of various proportions of land-derived detrital particles and debris of older rocks. These were cemented together (in layers or stata) usually by pressure of weight until, under compaction, they hardened.

In the case of Wenlock limestone containing a high proportion of fossilised remains with a high calcium content, for example coral and seashells, the limestone became rich in calcium carbonate.[1]

The word 'lime' is commonly used to mean not only calcium carbonate which, as will be appreciated from the previous paragraph, is the chief constituent of limestone, but also calcium oxide and calcium hydroxide.

Calcium Carbonate [$CaCO_3$] This takes the form of natural limestone and for use is ground to a fine powder. A good example of Wenlock limestone is almost pure calcium carbonate with a content in excess of 93%.[2]

Calcium Oxide [CaO] This is known as burnt lime or quicklime and is obtained by heating the crushed or broken stone in a kiln to a temperature of around 900 degrees Celsius (1652 Fahrenheit). This process is called calcination and it may be carried out in several types of kilns which could be either intermittent or continuous in their workings.[3]

Calcium Hydroxide [$Ca(OH)_2$] This is burnt lime with water added to it either when it is obtained from the kiln or at the point of use. The result of this mixture (called slaking) is a vigorous chemical action with the lime expanding quickly, becoming crumbly and giving off a great deal of heat, the end product being calcium hydroxide or hydrated lime.[4]

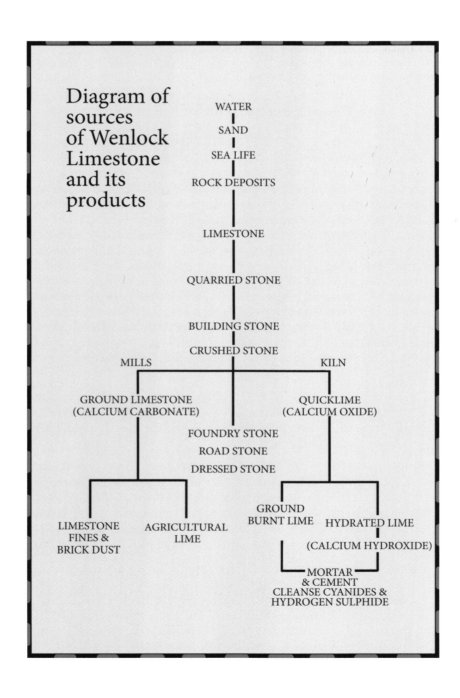

Diagram of
sources
of Wenlock
Limestone
and its
products

WATER

SAND

SEA LIFE

ROCK DEPOSITS

LIMESTONE

QUARRIED STONE

BUILDING STONE

CRUSHED STONE

MILLS   KILN

GROUND LIMESTONE
(CALCIUM CARBONATE)   QUICKLIME
(CALCIUM OXIDE)

FOUNDRY STONE

ROAD STONE

DRESSED STONE

LIMESTONE
FINES &
BRICK DUST   AGRICULTURAL
LIME   GROUND
BURNT LIME   HYDRATED LIME

(CALCIUM HYDROXIDE)

MORTAR
& CEMENT
CLEANSE CYANIDES &
HYDROGEN SULPHIDE

The Properties of Wenlock Limestone

References and Sources

1   A.E. Truman, *Geology in England and Wales* (London, Pelican, 1963)
2   Geological Survey (Shrewsbury District), 1938
3   *Encyclopaedia Britannica*
4   *Encyclopaedia Britannica*

Methods of Preparation

Calcium Carbonate To produce calcium carbonate (ground lime-stone) the raw material is first transported from the place of extraction to a primary crusher which reduces the size of the stone to between 100 and 200 mm. The crushing machine is usually of a jaw type and works in such a way that one jaw is fixed and the other moves to and fro by means of short and heavy cranks or toggles, so that very great pressure is placed on the material between the jaws. The limestone is then processed through a secondary crusher to further reduce its size.

After the crushing process, the stone is again transported, this time to a grinding mill. The original grinding mills were of the roller type (with a throughput of between 12 and 20 tons per hour) much on the same principle as a flour mill, which reduced the limestone to a powder of around 150 microns. With roller-type mills the limestone had to be reasonably dry for the milling to be effective. This resulted in two quarries in the 1950s and '60s employing oil-fired drying facilities. In later years hammer mills were employed. The throughput was around the same but the advantage of a hammer mill was that the stone could be fed in larger sizes (up to 100 mm) and also this type of mill could handle damp material, the induced draught from the hammers having a drying effect. Propulsion of the machinery was by means of electric motors, although in the period after the Second World War diesel engines were used in some quarries.

When the grinding process is completed, the ground lime (as the material is now called) is once again transported, usually by conveyor belt, to storage hoppers. The hoppers are so constructed that road vehicles can load the lime from beneath them.

The whole of this method, which is still used to produce calcium carbonate, was employed in the Wenlock quarries only in the last 50 working years of these quarries. Prior to that time, milled calcium carbonate as such was not produced, principally because demand did not justify the installation of costly machinery.[1]

Calcium Oxide A kiln is basically a receptacle in which a fire can be kindled, and to which fuel and limestone can be added, resulting in the raw limestone being converted under extreme heat to calcium oxide. The lime kiln used in Wenlock quarries was a vertical structure and shaped much like an inverted cone and ranging in size from three to 25 metres in height and three to seven metres in diameter at its mouth or top. Many theories have been advanced for the ideal shape, but the chief aims were to maintain the calcining temperature with fuel economy and to achieve good lime flow without 'hangup', that is, failure of the burnt lime to settle for drawing off at the base. It is constructed from limestone and, because of the lack of hard building stone locally, lined with firebricks, into which a stoking flue (usually on the side of the prevailing wind) is built.

An intermittent burning kiln, known locally as a 'pot' kiln, was usually sited at the side of the rock face from which the limestone was being quarried, the back of the wall (the kiln bank) resting on the hillside to facilitate the loading of the open kiln. At some sites, however, special earth ramps had to be constructed to allow the stone to be carried to the kiln top, whilst at other quarries the kilns were sited some distance away from the quarry face.

The charge was loaded into the kiln at the upper end and consisted of alternate layers of limestone (usually 10 to 15 cm in size and laid in such a way that the stone was standing on end; this was to facilitate burning) and either coke or slack coal, usually in proportion of one of fuel to three or four of limestone.

Coke was cheaper than coal as a fuel but had the disadvantage of contaminating the lime with sulphur and ash, whilst the ash from coal was virtually indistinguishable from burnt limestone. The charge was prevented from falling through into the adit (a small tunnel serving one or more kilns) by a grate or draw-hole built into the foot of the kiln. When the kiln was fully charged, a fire raised on brick-ends 30 cm or more above the kiln floor to help the burning process was lit at the base of the kiln; this spread gradually to the contents above and the whole charge was heated to a bright red or even a white heat. An alternative method of lighting the kiln was to kindle a fire in the bottom and then add the stone later. Overburden (waste mantle) was often placed at the top and to the front of the kiln to ensure the fire spread evenly.

About eight to 14 days was needed for calcination to take place, depending on the force and the direction of the draught for the fire. After a cooling period the charge was withdrawn from the bottom through the grate, the residue being some 60% plus of the original whole.[2] The removal of the burnt lime through the grate or draw-hole could be an unpleasant task. Men doing this job often protected their

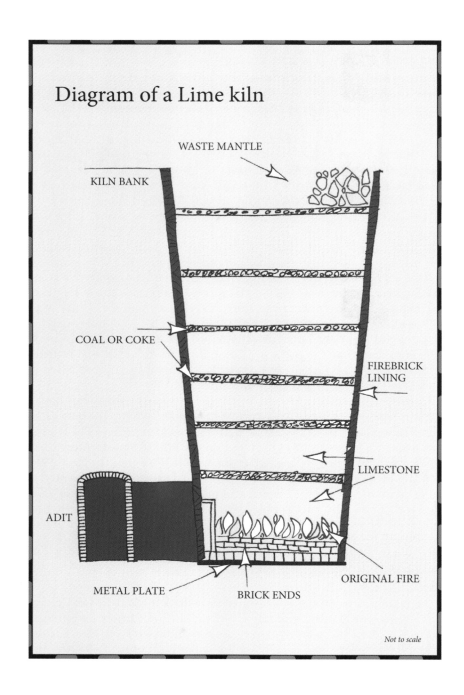

Diagram of a Lime kiln

WASTE MANTLE

KILN BANK

COAL OR COKE

FIREBRICK
LINING

LIMESTONE

ADIT

ORIGINAL FIRE

METAL PLATE

BRICK ENDS

Not to scale

This Wenlock quarry worker stands in front of the adit ready to shovel the burnt lime into the cart behind him.

faces from the heat by either greasing their skin or protecting their faces with a damp cloth.[3]

Although the charging of a pot kiln could have produced anything between two and 20 tons of lime (depending on the capacity of the kiln) the method was wasteful of fuel because the kiln had to be heated up for each loading, and there was the added problem of heat loss due to the kiln's wide mouth in relation to its depth. Also the lime produced was liable to be variable in quality, being either underburnt at the top or overburnt at the bottom.[4] For these reasons and to obtain a steady flow of lime, continuous or 'running' lime kilns were introduced after the middle of the eighteenth century. These were built on the same lines as a pot kiln (with the notable exception of two quarries where a steel cylindrical kiln was used) with a grid at the base through which the lime could be drawn off continuously. As the lime in the kiln became less, so more stone and fuel was added at the top. Thus a lime kiln of this nature could be worked indefinitely. Continuous burning kilns (with capacities up to 80 tons) were appreciably larger than intermittent burning kilns.[5]

Although this method of producing lime in Wenlock quarries was used for over 500 years, the burning of limestone has now been abandoned. The last lime kiln fires died in the mid 1960s.

Calcium Hydroxide In this process, freshly calcined lime was crushed to a powder then allowed to come into contact with a regulated supply of water. As previously mentioned, this is called slaking and the end product is hydrated lime.

The advantage of hydrated lime is that the product can be transported in bags without much danger of being damaged by dampness, and the quality of the lime could be made to conform to a standard specification.[6]

In days gone by, for most purposes, burnt or quicklime was slaked, usually by the purchaser at the point of use, by adding water to piles of lime and turning the heap with a shovel. The quality of the product then depended in large measure upon the skill and judgment of the workman.[7]

Hydrated lime was produced in Wenlock quarries only to a limited extent, and production had ceased entirely by the 1950s.[8]

References and Sources

1   G. Chegwen, general manager, Ridge Limestone Co., 1972
2   D. Watkins, foreman, Wm. Hayes & Co. Ltd, 1965
3   G.H. Griffith, ex-quarryman, Westwood Quarry, 1986
4   Watkins
5   G.D. Cooke, ex-quarryman, Westwood Quarry, 1989
6   *Encyclopaedia Britannica*
7   Watkins
8   W. Pitcher, ex-quarryman, Shadwell Quarry, 1973

The Industrial Uses of Wenlock Limestone

Building Not surprisingly, Wenlock limestone was first used for building purposes, as from the earliest times man has built his home from the nearest and most accessible material; and although originally this may have been mud, thatch, wood or wattle and daub, in later years, certainly for the founders of institutions and for the more prosperous of individuals, stone became a symbol of affluence and permanency. Some of the oldest and most important buildings in the town are either partly or wholly constructed from local limestone, as indeed some of the lesser buildings were after the dissolution of the monasteries when the ruined Priory became the nearest and easily the most accessible 'quarry'. As previously mentioned, the parish church is a good example of an old building with local stone in its structure; so too is the Corn Exchange. The Wenlock Railway Company also used local stone for the construction of its station buildings and bridge abutments. Three further good examples of buildings constructed from Wenlock limestone are the cemetery chapel and the hospital, built in 1890 and 1903 respectively, and, more recently, Manor Court retirement homes.

Limestone has also been used, to a very limited extent, for stone walling, examples of which can be seen on Blakeway Hollow Lane, at Tickwood and on the crest of the Edge at Westwood.

In normal building procedures mortar was required for binding stones together. The early manufacture of mortar would probably account for the first lime kilns being built in the area. It would most likely have been a horizontal 'clamp' kiln, an easily built contrivance of turf and earth, the earliest of which are recorded being at Wyke in 1523.[1] They would then have been called 'calciformium' or 'lyme putts'.[2] Mortar is made by mixing slaked lime with water and sand (usually by volume of one part lime to three parts sand). On exposure to the air it sets and becomes hard, partly as a result of normal drying and partly due to the absorption by the lime of carbon dioxide from the air.[3] Most of the older buildings in the town have had mortar used as a cementing material in their construction. Indeed as lately as 1937–8 mortar from local lime was used in the building of the Stretton Road housing estate, later named Havelock Crescent.[4]

This limestone abutment, built c. 1864, is all that remains of the railway bridge in Sheinton Street.

The Manor Court retirement homes were faced with Wenlock limestone.

The cemetery chapel was built in 1890 with Wenlock limestone.

Agriculture The next major use of Wenlock limestone would most likely have been in agriculture, as the use of lime on the land as an aid to crop growth is an ancient feature of good farming practice. In fact, the liming of agricultural land was known and appreciated long before the most active days of the pioneer agrarian improvers; for example, there is evidence of liming on the Dodington Estate in Shropshire in the 1340s.[5] A commentary on certain parishes in the Lothians in 1627 contains references to 'lyming' and the use of lime for 'guidding' the land.[6] In 1776 one to two wagon-loads of lime per acre was being spread and by the early 1800s 72–80 bushels was the going rate.[7]

Lime (burnt, hydrated or ground) is used to combat acidity in soils. Soils become acid, particularly light, sandy soils and soils at high elevation, if the lime content is low. Although most species and varieties

Dry-stone walling on Wenlock Edge.

of plants will tolerate a modest range of acidity, there are many crops which will not thrive under acid conditions. For example, barley, sugar beet and lucerne will not prosper in acid soils. Soils will also gradually lose lime by leaching, cropping, the feeding of livestock (dairy cows can take up to 80 kg of lime from soil per annum) and manuring, i.e. by the continued application of sulphate ammonia.[8]

However, lime for use on farming land could be misused too. At the July 1843 meeting of the Wenlock Farmers' Club, a Mr Newham of Shrewsbury, giving a talk entitled 'Agricultural Chemistry' referred to 'the evil practice of first spreading lime on fallow and then carting muck and spreading it on top of the lime, and carting muck together with lime to form compost heaps with the soil'.

Originally all lime used for soil fertilisation was burnt lime, and it appears that when limestone was burnt for mortar (and, to a much lesser extent, for use as a whitewash) the less pure lime was sold for fertiliser.[9] Particularly was this so before the widespread use of coal and coke in the kiln, when timber was the fuel used and great quantities were required (resulting in a great deal of ash in the lime) to reach the temperature needed for calcination to take place. For example, two cubic metres of oak (about 1,500 kg) or over three cubic metres of fir (about two tonnes) were needed to produce a tonne of lime in a pot kiln, whereas only 0.25 cubic metres of coal would have produced the same amount of lime.[10]

In the immediate post Second World War years lime was spread locally with an ex-Canadian Chevrolet 6×6-wheel-drive vehicle.

Ex-American GMC 6-wheel-drive vehicles like this were also used for limespreading around Wenlock just after the Second World War.

In recent times (post Second World War) the majority of the lime produced from Wenlock quarries for use in agriculture has been ground limestone, containing around 86% calcium carbonate with a neutralising value of about 50 to 60. This was spread on the land by mechanical spreader. The first type of spreaders (employed immediately after the war years) were a spinning contraption utilising the rear axle of a car. These spinners were towed behind a lorry or a tractor and trailer. The drive for spinning was from the wheels of the contraption via the differential axle which rotated a plate spreading the lime, the lime being shovelled on to the plate by a workman standing on the rear of the lorry or trailer. By the late 1940s special vehicles were being produced for the purpose. The first of these were two-wheel-drive lorry chassis on which a hopper with a moving floor (a continuous rubber belt) and spinning unit was built. Also, after the Second World War, many ex-W.D. four- and six-wheel-drive vehicles were pressed into service as lime spreaders, their payloads varying between two and eight tons. By the late 1950s interest had turned to tractor and trailer spreaders, with the lime being transported to the spreader on site by tipper lorry. The two main reasons for employing tractor spreaders were: a) in wet weather the tractor units did less damage to the land than the heavier lorry spreaders, and b) with the emergence of tipping lorries of greater capacity continually replenishing the spreaders on site, the operation became less costly.[11]

Smelting In all types of smelting in the foundry additions of limestone are made to the furnace charge. The object of this is to form a fluid slag with any sand or other impurities that may be associated with the pig or scrap iron. The limestone (of high quality, possessing around 90% calcium carbonate), which is rapidly calcined to lime in the furnace shaft, also forms a slag with any ash from the fuel used to fire the furnace. Before limestone was used to flux off the impurities they collected in the lower parts of the furnace as a kind of clinker, and every so often the hearth of the furnace had to be opened up to drag out this deposit, a task requiring hard manual labour.[12]

The use of Wenlock limestone as a medium for fluxing in the smelting of iron ore dates back certainly to the early eighteenth century when Abraham Darby I first used local stone in his iron foundry at Coalbrookdale.[13] The furnace charges then were: 98 lb (44 kg) of limestone to 224 lb (100 kg) of ironstone. By contrast, Anstice of Madeley was using one ton of limestone to three tons of ironstone in the early part of the nineteenth century,[14] but by 1873 the ratio had fallen to between 11 and 18 cwt (550 to 900 kg) to a ton of ironstone.[15]

Some 25,000 tons of fluxing stone was being produced per annum as lately as the 1970s.

Road construction Between 1700 and 1850 35,000 km (21,800 miles) of new roads were built in Britain, but for all that (in relative terms) very little serious work was done, either in the way of making new roads or in the maintenance of existing ones. This resulted in many traders and merchants in the nineteenth century complaining to their MPs 'that roads were very much destroyed by the carriage of salt, iron, chalk (lime) and other wares that made roads almost impassable and several carts and waggons have been broke and many horses lost'.[16] And in 1769 the *Ipswich Journal* told of a man, who having been thrown from his horse, fell into mud and filth in the road from which he suffocated. Locally, the deplorable state of Harley Hill in 1777 was a matter of concern.[17] These are examples which focused attention on the need for road improvements.

The first mention of Wenlock limestone being used in roadmaking was in the years 1806–7 when the Westwood Common Enclosure Act made reference to 'the allotment of stone pits for the repairing of roads'. In fact, in 1886 a half-acre of a quarry at Westwood (opposite Stretton Westwood turn) was reserved for the Much Wenlock Board of Health for the extraction of stone for roads in the Wenlock parish.[18]

The less fossiliferous limestone is best suited for road repairs and roadmaking, because fossils consist mainly of the mineral calcite, in which the cleavage is usually well developed, so that the rock fractures readily; if the fossils are fragmented and small the brittleness of the stone is considerably reduced. Thus the limestone will stand more wear from vehicle road wheels before being reduced to small fines or powder.[19] However, early road surveyors were not too keen on Wenlock limestone, save possibly for ballstone; they considered the limestone too soft, especially for use with tar.[20] In fact, in 1915 the council was buying dhu stone in preference to local stone and there were complaints from quarry owners in 1925 when road contractors were not using Wenlock limestone for the repair of local roads.[21]

Originally, stone quarried for road metal was carted to the roadside in large lumps and broken down either by a mobile stone breaker on site or by hand as required. For example, between the wars when the New Road was being resurfaced, the stone was transported from the quarries by horse and cart and then 'kibbled' by quarrymen – broken down by hammer to two-inch (50 mm) sizes and spread on the road[22] – and, in the widening of the Bridgnorth Road at the Gaskell corner in 1937, pitched '69' (six inch by nine inch) stone was used, the stone having been hand-selected in the quarry.[23] Now, however, all the stone is crushed mechanically to the appropriate size and is ready for use before it leaves the quarry.

Slabs, Pipes, Bricks and Artificial Stone To manufacture these products good quality limestone fines and dust are mixed with a

A demonstration of a mobile stone crusher that was used in roadmaking in the 1920s.

These Wenlock quarrymen used sledgehammers to smash the limestone by hand. It was then loaded into tubs and taken away by horse.

small quantity of cement and water (and dye if the product is to be coloured) and then pressed into moulds under extreme pressure. After either being steam-dried or left for a short time to dry out naturally, the product is ready for use.[24]

The first limestone building blocks were manufactured in the late 1940s (the now demolished Royal British Legion Hall in Smithfield Road was built with these blocks) but only some thirty years later was Wenlock limestone put extensively to this use. In three disused quarries manufacturing plants were installed for the making of bricks, paving slabs, drainage pipes and artificial stone. However, in 1992 the brick- and artificial stone-making facility was closed down and a similar fate awaited the paving slab plant in 1994. Poor trading conditions for these products was the reason given for their closure.[25]

Cement Cement was manufactured from Wenlock limestone from around 1890 to the early 1930s. The ingredients were: four parts ballstone, two parts bluestone (an inferior Wenlock limestone, bluish in colour and with a lower calcium carbonate content than ballstone and containing 10–20% silica, a necessary constituent for the making of this type of cement) and one part clay (specially imported from Cradley Heath or Rugby) which considerably raised the hydraulic properties (thus allowing the cement to harden in very moist conditions) of the finished product. To make the cement, the stone, in its natural state, had first to be weathered by being exposed to frost, sun and rain for two winters; this was done by leaving the stone in heaps around the quarry. It was then ground to powder and mixed with the clay and water to form a paste material; this was then shaped into brickettes approximately four inches (100 mm) square. The brickettes were then steam-dried before being fired in a cement kiln for about a week. After the burning process, the material was crushed, with the resulting powder being cement.[26]

Miscellaneous Uses Wenlock lime has been used (presumably) as an aid to decomposition, for a body was laid in a tomb of 'lyme and ston' near the 'altare' of the church in 1546,[27] and in the nineteenth century as a means of purifying the town sewer against smallpox[28] and in the process of tanning, for which the town was then well known. Lime was also used in the early life of the town's gasworks to remove toxic by-products from coal gas, such as hydrogen sulphide and carbon disulphide.[29] Also limestone was sold for poultry grit and grotto stone.[30]

References and Sources

1 Wynnstay box, National Library of Wales
2 F.B. Andrews, *The Medieval Builder and His Methods* (Oxford, OUP, 1976)
3 N. Davey, *A History of Building Materials* (London, Phoenix House)

4   Wenlock Council Minute Book, 5.1.1939
5   D.C. Cox et al., *Victoria History of the Counties of England: A History of Shropshire*, Vol. IV, 1989
6   B.C. Skinner, *The Lime Industry in the Lothians* (University of Edinburgh, 1969)
7   A. Young, *Tours of England and Wales* (1803)
8   'The Use of Lime in Agriculture', Ministry of Agriculture
9   D. Watkins, foreman, Wm. Hayes & Son Ltd, 1965
10 Davey
11 G. Chegwen, Ridge Limestone Co., 1972, and W.B. Phillips, Ridge Limestone Co., 1989
12 D.E. Howard (ed.), *Modern Foundry Practice* (Watford, Odhams Press, 1959)
13 B. Trinder, *The Industrial Revolution in Shropshire* (Chichester, Phillimore, 1973)
14 I. Brown, *Shropshire Magazine*, April 1965
15 Microfilm 109, Shrewsbury Local Studies Library
16 J. Nichol, *Developing Britain* (Oxford, B. Blackwell, 1983)
17 Trinder
18 Wenlock Sanitary Book, 27.9.1886
19 F.J. North, *Limestones* (London, Murby & Co., 1930)
20 T.H. Thompson, scrapbook, Wenlock Archives
21 Wenlock Council Minute Book, 28.4.1925
22 G.H. Griffith, ex-quarryman, Westwood Quarry, 1986
23 G.D. Cooke, ex-quarryman, Westwood Quarry, 1989
24 D.L. Pardoe, engineer, A.J. Mucklow & Co. Ltd, 1971
25 *Shropshire Star*, 4.2.1994
26 T. Langford, ex-quarryman, Bradley Quarry, 1965
27 Wenlock Church Archive, Wenlock Public Library (Reference)
28 Wenlock Council Minute Book, 14.3.1887
29 Wenlock Gasworks Account Book and R.W. Collingwood, 1994
30 Moore & Shields billhead, 1930

The General Background of the Industry

In the early days the quarries (frequently referred to then and until recent times as the 'Rocks') were small and were worked in a primitive way. Often people combined other occupations such as cow-keeping and beer-selling with quarrying and lime-burning,[1] and even with other sources of income it appears that quarrying and lime-burning on a small scale was not very profitable. There are numerous instances down the years of quarriers finding difficulty in making their enterprises pay. Just two examples: Francis Southerne, a 'lymemaker' who died in 1730, was heavily in debt[2] and John Bebb was described in the 1831 census as a 'pauper lime burner'. In fact, some of the smaller quarries, where burnt lime was the chief product, were not worked in the winter months. Tools for the extraction, transportation and processing of the stone, which remained in use until the introduction of mechanical appliances, were of the simple type. Old quarry inventories include rammer bars, heavy hammers, wheelbarrows and stone rakes.[3]

The first procedure in the quarrying of limestone is the removal of the layer of top soil from above the rock. This layer of soil is known as 'overburden' or 'bearing'. Originally shovels and wheelbarrows were required to remove between 20 and 500 mm (around one to 18 inches) of soil. Later the soil was usually removed by a bulldozer pushing a blade before it.

Although gunpowder was invented sufficiently early for there to be references to cannon in the stores of the Tower of London in 1388, it was not applied to the blasting of rock until early in the seventeenth century (in Saxony in 1627) and in this country it does not appear to have been used until a much later date.[4] Before the use of mechanical drilling (to insert the explosive charge) holes in the rock were bored by hand. The drilling of the hole, approximately 35 mm (1½ inches) in diameter, was often carried out by a two-man team; one man supported and turned the rammer bar or 'jumper', to which a leather tongue was often attached to avoid jarring, whilst the other wielded a seven to 11 kg (15 to 25 lb) hammer. The rammer bar was around two metres (6½ feet) in length and had two cutting edges at its point which were lubricated by water being poured down the hole.[5] Prior to the Great War, men who were working 'piecework' at this job in the Westwood and Presthope quarries often brought their drills and rammers down to the blacksmith's shop in St Mary's Lane to be sharpened. They would then return to their quarries by getting a free ride in the open trucks of the GWR goods train which travelled each morning to Westwood, Presthope and beyond.[6] It was not uncommon for the quarry 'blower', the quarryman responsible for detonating the explosive charges, to start work as early as four a.m. to ensure enough loose stone was ready for the start of the day's work.[7]

Before the use of gelignite and other modern explosives, black powder was used for blasting the rock. This was ignited by a naked fuse which had been inserted down each vertically drilled and charged hole. When fuses were not available it was usual to use wheat straw stems joined together and filled with black powder.[8]

Inevitably, with such haphazard use of dangerous explosives, it was not uncommon for accidents to happen. At Bradley Quarry in July 1832 for example, Thomas Trevor was killed in a blasting accident. Trevor was feeding powder down a bore hole whilst his assistant, Joe Hill, was waiting beside him with a lighted piece of paper. A spark from the paper prematurely ignited the powder with the result that Trevor made an instant and non-returnable journey to his maker.[9] Two years later William Carter was blown up whilst blasting rock at an unspecified quarry. He was drunk at the time and a colleague said: 'He [Carter] was blown to a great height and landed 20 yards from the blast hole and did not speak again.'[10] At the Lilleshall Quarry, H. Lilyman injured his hand when an explosive charge did not go off as quickly as usual,[11] and back at Bradley Quarry, around the turn of the century, an unnamed quarry worker injured his arms and eyes in a blasting accident.[12] Again in the Lilleshall Quarry, in 1908, Richard Jones died from injuries sustained in a blasting accident. Two versions circulated regarding the cause: one was smoking near the bore hole and the other a faulty fuse. Whatever the cause, the whole workforce was allowed to attend his funeral with twelve being pall-bearers.[13] Two years later, again at the Lilleshall Quarry, Frank Skutt was seriously injured in an explosion and was conveyed to the recently opened Lady Forester Hospital.[14] In the early 1930s Tommy Weaver lost half an ear through being too hasty in lighting black powder at the Plough Quarry, and Albert Skutt, in the Westwood Quarry in 1936, was blinded. Whilst preparing for a popping operation (letting off a small charge to dislodge stone on a quarry face bench) Skutt accidentally hit the percussion cap of the detonator (by this time blasting had moved on from the days of black powder) when in the process of putting it down the bore hole.[15] In another accident at Cox's Rock in January 1940, Tommy Anson was badly injured and was off work for six months. He was the 'blower' responsible for 'plastering' (placing small charges under dislodged rocks lying on the quarry floor in order to reduce their size). He either miscounted the exploding charges or thought one had failed to go off. When he went to inspect, the elusive charge exploded.[16] The last fatal accident occurred in the Ballstone Quarry in 1939 when Harold Firmstone was killed whilst carrying explosives.[17]

On a lighter note, one irate quarryman, not liking the unenviable task of emptying the quarry bucket toilet, decided the most thorough and efficient way was to use a stick of explosive.[18] Until recent years each quarry stored its own explosives in a 'powder house'.

In more recent times the limestone was bored with a pneumatic drill and the explosive detonated electrically by remote control.

After blasting operations the quarryman had to reduce, either at the quarry face or kiln top, the size of some of the limestone by wielding sledge hammers or by using bars and wedges. Most of the men cut their own hazel wood staves for their hammers as evidently this wood is a good absorbent of jarring.[19]

Transportation of the limestone from the quarry floor to the kiln top and beyond, depended on the site and the date. In the very early days transport would have been by packhorse, using special horse panniers or 'panyery's'[20] or horse and cart. The cost of keeping a horse for working in a quarry was 4/8 (24p) per week in 1842.[21] The

The powder house at Farley Quarry c. 1980.

The old powder house in Westwood Quarry which dated from c. 1880.

This Wenlock quarryman holds a sledgehammer and an implement for
splitting rock.

cost of keeping a donkey may have been cheaper as evidently one was employed at the Knowle Quarry as late as the first quarter of the twentieth century.[22]

From around the middle of the nineteenth century until after the Second World War, narrow (two foot) gauge tramways were the chief means of transport, although as early as 1801 a plateway was being used on an inclined plane between the crest and the foot of the scarp slope of Wenlock Edge.[23] The early trucks on the tramways would probably have been small, four-wheeled vehicles with square or rectangular wooden bodies, but in later years a V-shaped hopper type, of one to one and half tons capacity, was introduced. The design was for ease of unloading, the body swinging on a frame. If they were not pulled by a horse, these trucks (often called 'tubs' or 'boxes') were either pushed by hand or, in the last few years of their use, pulled along by means of a wire rope attached to a stationary engine, or in the case of West-wood Quarry, hauled by a petrol-engined locomotive, the last driver of which was 'Codger' Luscott. This loco was thought to be of German origin and was sold for scrap in 1954.[24] The last tramways were used in the 1950s at Westwood Quarry and at Wenlock (Hayes) Quarry. After-wards the raw material was transported from the base of the quarry face to the processing plant by motor truck or dumper, the loading of the dumper being carried out by a mechanical grab or motor shovel.

The allocation of workmen's tasks must clearly have varied from quarry to quarry. However, the typical division of labour seems to have been fairly consistent since the early systematic working of quarries until after the Second World War, when the advent of mechanical handling of the limestone revolutionised the industry. A quarrymaster describing his quarry and limeworks in Scotland in 1757 wrote: '...two men for boring and blasting, three for breaking and filling the one that draws the lime from the "kill", slakes and delivers and one more that has a two horse cart for loading the stone from the quarry to the level at the top of the "kill"'. With this team he considered it a good day's work to break ten 'bolls' of stone (about 2½ tons of lime).[25] Apart from the very small, one- or two-man-operated concerns, and the very big enterprises, these arrangements would have been typical in most Wenlock quarries.

The Coalbrookdale Company was paying quarrymen one shilling and fourpence (7p) per day in 1776,[26] but by 1830 the going rate appears to have been between 10/- (50p) and 11/- (55p) per week with somewhat less for the lowest paid workers at the kiln head.[27] This compares with a wage of 3/- (15p) per day at the end of the nineteenth century, 4½d to 6d (2p to 3p) per hour in the early 1920s, 9d to 10d (around 5p) per hour in the early 1930s, £3 to £4 per week prior to the outbreak of the Second World War, £7 per week in the immediate post-war period, 3/- (15p) per hour in the 1950s and something in excess of £30 per week in the 1970s. In the latter three instances the working day varied between eight and ten hours per day and also production bonuses were paid.[28] Up to 1939, however, men were often employed on a 'piecework' basis, usually being paid by the tub or box of limestone extracted or by the tub of lime taken from the kiln. At the beginning of the 1920s quarry workers were being paid 10d (4p) per tub, having first broken by hand the limestone into acceptable sizes, (around 6 inches or 15 cm for burning). Ten years later the rate had risen to 7d and 1/3 (3½p and 6½p) for lump and broken stone respectively.[29] The tub was either pushed by hand or hauled by a horse along a tramway to the kiln top or loading wharf, the horse usually being led by the youngest employee, often a youth having recently left school. When times were hard, through inclement weather or the depressed state of the industry, pieceworkers often supplemented their incomes by working on local farms hoeing, hedge brushing, pulling root crops, harvesting grain etc.[30] The more innovative sought other ways of increasing their income. In the poor times of the early 1930s four quarriers, George Cooke, George (Nick) Walters, Jack Langford and Baden Minton, all working at the Westwood Quarry, regularly went morris dancing. Minton played the 'bones' whilst a friend, Bonar Merrick, was coerced into playing the 'squeeze box'. Up to 12/- (60p) could be earned between the five in the streets of Shrewsbury on a Saturday afternoon.[31] Because of serious unemployment in the quarries in 1923, the Town Council stimulated demand for stone by asking the surveyor to seek a grant from the County Council to repair local roads,[32] and regular employment before the First World War was even more scarce because in 1909 three notable ladies of the town, Lady Milnes Gaskell, Mrs Cooke (wife of Alderman Cooke of the Cooke clock and Corris House fame) and Mrs Danks (wife of the National School headmaster), opened a soup kitchen for the children of the unemployed.[33]

Abraham Darby was costing limestone for fluxing (delivered to the furnace at Coalbrookdale) at 4/- (20p) per ton in 1718.[34] By 1761 the cost had risen to between 3/6 (17½p) and 4/- (20p) ex-quarry, whilst in Shropshire as a whole agricultural lime in 1776 was 11/6 (57½p) per cartload (around 40 to 50 bushels) ex-kiln.[35] In 1827 lime for mortar was 6d (2½p) per bushel and in 1848 8/- (40p) per ton.[36] The price of lime could well have been cheaper but for the high cost of fuel.[37] The cost of coal, however, was considerably reduced with the coming of the railway; nevertheless, the price more than doubled in the first quarter of the twentieth century, from 13/- (65p) to 32/- (£1.60) per ton.[38] In the early 1850s a cartload of lime (about 1 to 1½ tons) was delivered from one of the quarries on the Bank (off Stretton Road) to the gasworks in Barrow Street for 11/- (55p).[39] This appears quite expensive; however, one ton at that time was probably equal to 3,120 lb rather than 2,240 latterly.

The arrival of the railway considerably reduced transport costs. Fluxing stone being sent to South Staffordshire via the Severn Valley route was costing 4d (2p) per ton/mile in 1862.[40] In 1864 100 tons of limestone cost £5 to transport by rail to Buildwas.[41] By 1873 fluxing stone was selling for 4/6 (23p) per ton plus transport costs of 2/3 (11p) per ton bulk to Wolverhampton via Lightmoor.[42] This compares to the local road transport rate, as recently as 1906, of 9d (3½p) for one man and horse to 1/1 (5½p) for a two-horse team.[43] By the 1920s costs had risen to 20/- (£1) per ton of lime and between 5/- (25p) and 10/- (50p) for stone, all ex-works with added transport charges averaging 6d (2½p) per ton/mile.[44] In the immediate pre-1939–45 war years £2 per ton for burnt lime was about the going rate, increasing to £4 and £1 per ton respectively for burnt and ground lime in the 1950s, whilst stone for fluxing and roadmaking was considerably cheaper.[45] For example, in 1937, ½ inch (13 mm) chippings (to repair the Station Road) were costing 6/- (30p) per ton delivered.[46] In the Second World War years, under the Land Fertility Scheme, bagged lime (calcium hydroxide) cost, after a 50% subsidy, around £1.30 per ton.[47] In the early years cartloads were often quoted as opposed to actual weight, because in most of the quarries weighing facilities did not exist. Indeed, the comment was made that: 'lime is seldom measured at all at many of the limeworks, being thrown into the cart and the quantity judged by the eye, he who has the largest cart getting the best bargain.' However, after the railway came, weighbridges were available both to the public and quarrymasters at Wenlock and Presthope stations.

The general trend of the industry seems to have been that, prior to Darby's iron-smelting discovery, which in consequence created a greater demand for limestone, the quarries around Wenlock produced lime and limestone chiefly for building and agricultural purposes, although it should not be overlooked that iron-smelting furnaces requiring limestone in their charges existed at Coalbrookdale before Darby's discovery in 1709.[48]

Reflecting the demand for limestone for fluxing, thus creating new jobs in the quarries, the parish population rose by 22% in the years 1801–31.[49]

Around the middle of the nineteenth century there was, to the north of the town and nearer the ironworks, a general shortage of good limestone for fluxing, but with the building of the railway in 1862–4 the problem was somewhat resolved as then the limestone south-west of Wenlock became both more accessible and cheaper to transport. But it was still not as cheap as limestone bought by the iron foundries from North Wales.[50] Also, in the wake of the railway, larger enterprises interested in fluxing stone production became established in what was hitherto the domain of the local quarrier and lime-burner. However, the railway came too late to benefit from the peak years of

The weighbridge in the railway goods yard was used by Hayes's Wenlock Quarry.

the iron trade. From the 1860s onwards demand gradually declined, in part because by that time Germany and the USA in particular had started their own heavy industries which resulted in a cutback in iron production locally. This caused a decline in fluxing demand, which was reflected in the reports of the directors of the Much Wenlock and Severn Valley Railway. Firstly in 1863, when they made the observation: 'No ironmasters have availed themselves to the Railway Company for the carriage of limestone to their furnaces.'[51] This was because the spur from Buildwas to Coalbrookdale (which would give direct access, not only to the East Shropshire coalfield, but also to the main Shrewsbury–Birmingham line) had not been completed. Secondly, in 1867 the directors reported with regret, 'That owing to the depression in the iron trade gross receipts for haulage are down on the previous year'.[52] Thirdly, in 1870 they stated, 'The diminution in the traffic still continues and chiefly arises from the falling off in the limestone trade.'[53] To add weight to their concern the *Borough of Wenlock Express* of 16 December 1876 stated that 'mills and forges are almost destitute of orders and slackness is the rule'.

The demand for agricultural lime was even less brisk. In the 1820s there occurred a general falling-off in the requirement for lime, due to a combination of over-liming in previous years, over-production of cereals and, as it probably concerned Wenlock quarries directly, the adverse effect of the 1822 Turnpike Act which made lime subject to

Turnpike Duty, which penalised farmers and producers alike. From the 1830s to the 1870s trade picked up, albeit modestly, but towards the end of the century a recession was again experienced (aggravated by cheap grain imports from Australia, New Zealand and Canada) and this lasted until 1914 and the commencement of the First World War. At the start of the war farmers were only producing 20% of the nation's wheat requirements and as a whole could only feed the country for 125 days.[54] Demand for home-produced food between 1914 and 1918 stimulated the lime trade, but this demand fell away again in the depression years of the twenties and thirties. A further factor that depressed the lime trade in the early part of this century was the mistaken belief that chemical fertilisers made lime unnecessary.[55] A welcome hiccup occurred in 1927 when the Allscott beet factory was opened. Farmers growing sugar beet needed lime to combat acidity in the soil.[56] It was 1939, however, when the agricultural lime trade took a dramatic turn for the better. This was because with the outbreak of the Second World War it became necessary again to produce more home-grown food. A subsidy of £2 per acre was introduced to encourage farmers to plough permanent grassland for cereals.[57] From the middle of the war until the mid-sixties (the peak year was 1956) ground limestone for agricultural fertiliser was at a premium. But demand was seasonal, spring and autumn being the peak periods, leaving the quarries virtually idle in the winter months. Burnt lime could not be produced in sufficient quantity and also it became too costly to manufacture. However, after the mid-sixties, due to a general cutback in government subsidies to farmers to purchase lime (at its height the subsidy was 65%), plus a mild recession in the farming industry, the agricultural lime trade took another downward turn.

Nevertheless, with the nearness of the Wenlock limestone quarries to what was Dawley New Town and later Telford New Town development, plus a greater demand generally for roadmaking materials, a dramatic switch was made to the production of aggregates, hard core and roadmaking stone. This probably saved the Wenlock limestone trade from virtual extinction as these products became the mainstay of the industry.

References and Sources

1   Sundry 18th- and 19th-century trade directories
2   S. Mullins, curator, Much Wenlock Museum, 1981
3   Inventory, Bradley Quarry, 1889
4   F.J. North, *Limestones* (Murby & Co., 1930)
5   N. Davey, *A History of Building Materials* (London, Phoenix House, 1961)
6   L. Hanson, 1973
7   G.H. Griffith, ex-quarryman, Westwood Quarry, 1986
8   F. Stretton, ex-clerk, Shadwell Quarry, 1968

9 Inquisition, Wenlock Archives
10 Inquisition
11 T.H. Thompson, scrapbook, Wenlock Archives
12 Thompson
13 Thompson
14 Thompson
15 G.D. Cooke, ex-quarryman, Westwood Quarry, 1986
16 D. Watkins, foreman, Wm. Hayes & Son Ltd, 1965.
17 Cooke
18 Watkins
19 Stretton
20 F.R. Andrews, *The Medieval Builder and His Methods* (Oxford, OUP, 1976)
21 Wenlock Farmers Club, Wenlock Archives, 1842
22 Hanson
23 Shropshire Records Office
24 D.A. Holmes, thesis, Ironbridge Gorge Museum
25 B.C. Skinner, *The Lime Industry in the Lothians* (University of Edinburgh, 1969)
26 A. Young, *Annals of Agriculture*, London, 1784–1809
27 Watkins
28 H. Edwards, P.S.J. Platt and J. Moore, ex-quarrymen
29 Cooke
30 T. Langford, ex-quarryman, Bradley Quarry, 1965
31 Cooke
32 Thompson
33 Thompson
34 A. Raistrick, *Dynasty of Ironfounders* (Longman, Green, 1953)
35 Young
36 Raistrick
37 North
38 Wenlock Sanitary Book, 30.5.1907 and 4.8.1924
39 Much Wenlock Gas Company Account Book
40 Microfilm 113, Shrewsbury Local Studies Library
41 Microfilm 113
42 Microfilm 109, Shrewsbury Local Studies Library
43 Wenlock Sanitary Book, 7.6.1906
44 C.R.H. Kane and G.H. Griffith, sales material, 1986
45 Watkins
46 Wm. Hayes & Co., statement to Wenlock Council, 2.6.1937
47 Much Wenlock parish magazine, March 1943
48 Raistrick
49 *Victoria County History of Shropshire*, Vol. V
50 Microfilm 109
51 Microfilm 113
52 Microfilm 113
53 University of Hull Reference Library
54 C. Dakers, *The Countryside at War 1914–18* (London, Constable, 1987)
55 P. Stamper, *The Farmer Feeds Us All* (Shrewsbury, Shropshire Books, 1989)
56 *Victoria County History*
57 *Victoria County History*

Gazetteer of Limestone Working Sites

A fold-out map of the sites mentioned is inside the back cover. Arrangement is by geographical position, from south-west of Much Wenlock at Hilltop to near Tickwood in the north-east. The numbers following the site names are the Ordnance Survey six-figure grid references.

HILLTOP QUARRY 575968 This is one of the oldest quarrying sites, dating back certainly to 1714, when the personages of Richard Powell, Edward Gorton and Edward Thomas were the lime-burners there. For this privilage they were each paying 13/- (65p) per annum rent to the Manor of Wenlock.[1]

By 1770 William Hayward was the quarrier and lime-burner, and it appears that he was still there in 1807 when the area was probably better known (for obvious reasons) as 'Balled Rock'.[2]

According to the tithe map, William Hayward was still at Hilltop in 1847, but the number of intervening years suggest that this Hayward would probably have been a son or other relative. Anyway, at that date quarrying was taking place both to the north and south of the main road near to where the site of the tourist look-out is now, and in the years 1851–5 the rent Hayward was paying George Benson of Lutwyche Estate amounted to £15 annually,[3] a near two-and-a-quarter thousand per cent increase on the rent first recorded nearly 150 years earlier. The kilns were to the south and near to the roadside. They were not to remain there long, however, as they were destroyed by the quarrying operations of the Lilleshall Company after 1862. Traces of coal and ash from these kilns was visible near the roadside in Lilleshall Quarry.

The Hayward family continued quarrying at Hilltop certainly until 1856.[4] Thereafter the quarry seems to have slipped into oblivion, again partly due to the quarrying activities of the Lilleshall Company.

The workings on the north side of the road became known as 'the roadside waste' before the Wenlock Council made provision in 1923 for charabancs to use it.[5]

Mention should also be made of a small quarry situated near the Wenlock Edge Inn at Hilltop (571963). Very little is known about this site, but from evidence gleamed from the 1847 Tithe and 1902 OS maps, it was probably worked sometime between the middle and the close of the nineteenth century with possibly a Nathaniel Reece being a lime-burner there between 1855 and 1868.[6] However, it was reopened for a short period around 1920 for building stone required in the construction of the Birdwood and Allenby Cottages in East-hope.[7] Also in the late 1940s it was the home (parking facility) for Malscott Lime Spreaders.

References and Sources

1   Manor of Wenlock Survey 1714, National Library of Wales
2   Westwood Common Enclosure Act 1806–7
3   1851 Census
4   *Post Office Directory*, 1856
5   Wenlock Council Minute Book, 1.3.1923
6   Wenlock Rates Book, 1855, and *Slater's Directory*, 1868
7   T. Goodman Snr, farmer, Hilltop Farm, 1968

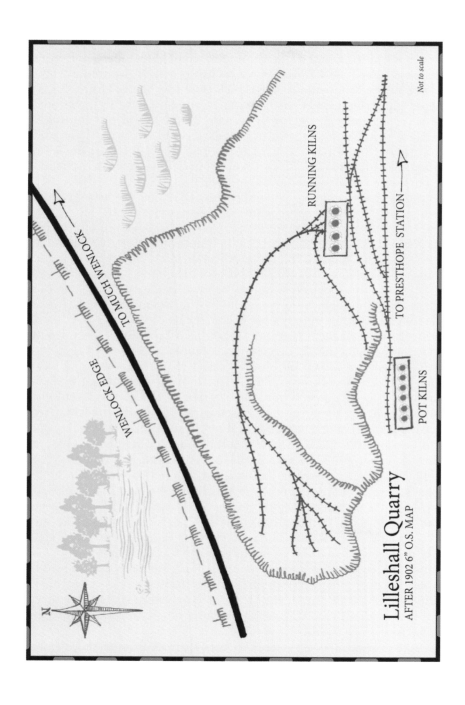

Lilleshall Quarry
AFTER 1902 6" O.S. MAP

Not to scale

TO MUCH WENLOCK

WENLOCK EDGE

RUNNING KILNS

POT KILNS

TO PRESTHOPE STATION

N

LILLESHALL QUARRY 576968 Although the Lilleshall Company, which had iron foundries in and around Priorslee, was interested in limestone production south of Wenlock as early as 1842,[1] it was not until 20 years later in 1862 that Moses George Benson, the local landowner from Lutwyche Hall, leased a parcel of land, known as 'Presthope Rocks', to the Rt Hon. the Earl of Granville, the latter being the head of the Lilleshall Company. The area was some 28 acres (around 11 hectares) in extent and lay to the south-east of the Much Wenlock to Church Stretton road. The rent was £500 per annum plus royalties of 4d (1½p) per 2,640 lb for all limestone extracted, and 12d (5p) per cartload of burnt lime made, a cartload to be comprised of 56 bushels.[2]

In retrospect this may have appeared an expensive lease, particularly as £10,000 was spent opening up the quarry,[3] but the lack of good limestone near its iron foundries, coupled with the notion that the new railway would give easy access to the limestone, probably persuaded the Lilleshall Company that it was worthwhile. Unfortunately, both railway spurs, from Presthope station to the quarry and across the river at Buildwas (which would have given a direct link to the East Shropshire coalfield), were not opened until December 1865.[4] Thus, in the first years of the quarry's life, when, incidentally, the quarry workers were the Lilleshall Company's own men brought in from around Priorslee,[5] production by necessity was limited.

Because a lot of the limestone proved of poor quality for fluxing (the Lilleshall puddlers preferred North Wales limestone) plus the fact that Benson's agent wanted royalties on the stone increased to 6d (2½p) per ton because, the agent argued, 1½ tons of limestone was needed to produce one ton of burnt lime, production at the quarry suddenly stopped in 1869. This was after some acrimonious correspondence between the Lutwyche Estate and the Lilleshall Company.[6]

The quarry reopened in 1873, when production exceeded 30,000 tons. A great deal of this tonnage was burnt for mortar and agricultural lime, two banks of kilns having been built in the same year.[7] The larger of the two, which comprised four running kilns (a massive 20 metres in height, but with varying diameters at their tops) was demolished in 1985 to make way for further quarrying operations. The smaller bank, comprising six pot kilns served by two adits, approximately four metres high, is still standing but in an advanced state of decay. Both these banks of lime kilns were served by a direct rail link to Presthope station, so allowing lime to be loaded straight from the kiln on to railway trucks.

In 1876 the Lilleshall Company was successful in getting its rent reduced by a half.[8] This was possibly because of the poor quality of some of the limestone and the depressed state of the iron trade at that time.

These pot kiln banks at the Lilleshall Quarry were built c. 1870.

On 27 July 1894 the dead body of William Morgan, who was a part-time quarrier and rabbit catcher, was found at the foot of the quarry face. It was thought he had fallen from the top of the quarry face the previous evening when inspecting snares. Coincidentally, his father had suffered a similar fate at the same place a few years previously.[9]

In 1896, the lease between M.G. Benson and the Lilleshall Company was renewed for a further 14 years. The new rent negotiated was £200 per annum. The royalty for limestone remained the same but for burnt lime it was increased to 6d (2½p) per 2,640 lb,[10] the reduced rent perhaps reflecting both the quality and quantity of limestone still available for extraction, and the increased royalty on burnt lime could have been the result of the protracted negotiations that took place between the agent for the Lutwyche Estate and the Lilleshall Company dating back nearly 30 years previously.

Notwithstanding poor trading conditions generally, around the start of the twentieth century Lilleshall Quarry appeared to be the most important undertaking of its kind south of Wenlock, with a weekly production of lime and limestone (most of the latter going for fluxing) of upwards of a thousand tons per week.[11] Most of the products were transported by rail in the company's own eight-ton trucks and in peak periods two trains would leave the quarry each day.[12] Nevertheless, some stone was sold locally. For example, in 1908, 50 tons of roadstone was supplied, at 3/6 (17½p) per ton, to repair the Woodhousefields road and five years later another 50-ton order was won from Wenlock Council for road repairs.[13]

Although evidently the lease officially expired in 1911, the quarry was still being worked in 1916.[14] At that time German prisoners of war could be seen, doubtless reluctantly, breaking stone in the quarry.[15] The quarry had, however, fallen into disuse by the end of the Great War, when the exposed area was 13 acres (5.2 hectares).[16] A possible reason why operations had ceased by that time was that the big call-up of able-bodied men for military service had resulted in a grave shortage of labour. The rail link between the quarry and Presthope station was lifted around 1917 because steel was needed for the war effort. After the war the Lilleshall Company apparently did not consider it a viable proposition to reopen the quarry, possibly due to poor trading conditions.[17]

After remaining unworked for nearly 60 years the quarry was given a new lease of life. The Ridge Limestone Company, which had obtained quarrying rights as far back as 1948,[18] commenced quarrying at the north end of the site in 1976, principally for aggregates. The English China Clay Company was the last quarrier, ceasing production in 1990 when the annual output was around 25,000 tons, virtually the whole of which was sold for roadstone or hardcore.[19]

Aggregate extraction in the Lilleshall Quarry in 1988.

References and Sources

1   B. Trinder, *The Industrial Revolution in Shropshire* (Chichester, Phillimore, 1973)
2   Box 809, Shropshire Records Office
3   Microfilm 113, Shrewsbury Local Studies Library
4   Microfilm 113
5   W.K.V. Gale & C.R. Nicholls, *The Lilleshall Company: A History 1764–1964* (Ashbourne, Moorland, 1979)
6   Microfilm 113
7   Microfilm 113
8   Box 809
9   T.H. Thompson, scrapbook, Wenlock Archives
10 Box 809
11 F. Stretton, ex-clerk, Shadwell Quarry, 1968
12 J. Watkins Snr, GWR engine driver, 1971
13 Wenlock Council Minute Book, 3.12.1908 & 4.12.1913
14 *Wildings Directory*, 1916
15 G.B. Cooke, ex-quarryman, Westwood Quarry, 1989
16 6-inch OS map, 1926
17 T. Goodman Snr, farmer, Hilltop Farm
18 *Bridgnorth Journal*, 21.5.1967
19 W.S. Hughes, foreman, Lea Quarry, 1988

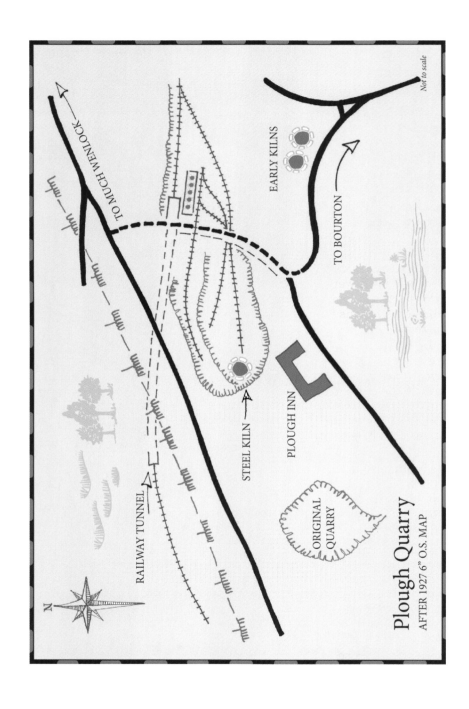

TO MUCH WENLOCK

EARLY KILNS

TO BOURTON

RAILWAY TUNNEL

STEEL KILN

PLOUGH INN

ORIGINAL QUARRY

N

Not to scale

Plough Quarry

AFTER 1927 6" O.S. MAP

PLOUGH QUARRY 583974 This site was named after the Plough Inn which once stood within drinking distance of the quarry, and before that it was known first as Quarry Piece,[1] then Five Chimneys Quarry,[2] after the row of cottages (demolished in the 1960s) which stood on the main road near the quarry, and latterly it has been referred to as Presthope Quarry.

There is a possibility that a Thomas Hayward (who was also renting nine labourers' cottages from the Lutwyche Estate at the time) could have been interested in limestone in this vicinity around 1778, also William Shirley in 1833,[3] Thomas Harrington (who was later to be found quarrying on the Bank) in 1838[4] and William George in 1841.[5] By 1847 Richard Meakin was renting a parcel of land for the extraction of limestone called 'Quarry Piece'.[6] This quarry was immediately north-east of the now demolished Presthope Farm and west of where the later, and more extensive, workings took place.

The present quarry appears to have come into existence around the 1850s when Joseph Beddoe and John Hayes were the quarriers.[7] Beddoe's kilns were near the Plough Inn[8] whilst Hayes's kilns could have been the ones unearthed in the 1970s (and later obliterated) when excavations were taking place to the south of the quarry on the north side of the original road leading to Bourton.

In June 1864 William Fields, of Quarry House, Shrewsbury, trading as Fields Mercantile Company, leased from M.G. Benson of Lutwyche Hall a parcel of land in the vicinity of the present quarry for seven years (to quote the lease: 'lying above and around the proposed railway tunnel') for the express purpose of quarrying limestone. The terms of the lease were: rent £200 per annum rising to £300 when the proposed railway was opened; royalties of 4d (2½p) per 2,640 lb of all limestone quarried and 12d (5p) per load (comprising 56 bushels) of lime sold. Also, the lessee had the power to lay a mineral line from Presthope station, which at a later date took place.[9] As will have been noted, the royalties were the same as for the Lilleshall Quarry. The lower rent reflected the smaller area of land under consideration, whilst the additional rent rising from £200 to £300 per annum when the railway came was because the limestone would be much easier and possibly cheaper to transport away then.

Fields' intention was to supply, via the railway, fluxing stone to Shropshire and Staffordshire ironworks, but because the limestone at the Plough proved to be of such poor quality, this venture never came to fruition. Having driven a 'gullet' through the entire length of the proposed quarry in an effort (unsuccessfully) to find good limestone, Fields closed the quarry after only three or four years and subleased it to a Mr Gough for a reduced yearly rental of £100. This was after spending £2,700 to open up the quarry and lay sidings from Presthope station. The quality of the limestone was so bad that samples sent to 25 Black Country ironworks were rejected, and the Old Park Ironworks at Stirchley, having tried 30 tons, 'would not have any more even if it were free!'[10] Gough's venture was no more successful and the quarry was closed and the sidings lifted by 1873.[11]

Whilst Gough was at the Plough there occurred a tragic accident in April 1869 when a man named Botfield, working on the kiln top, sank up to his knees in the burning lime. Evidently it was the habit of workers recharging running kilns to throw large lumps of coal on the lime and then get on top of the coal to break it. The quarry manager, at the risk of his own life, also went on top of the burning lime and caught hold of Botfield's hand, but was unable to pull him out. A few minutes later, however, he was rescued by means of ironstone rakes, but was so badly burned that he died within the hour.[12]

According to the 2½-inch OS map of 1889 the quarry was still dormant at that date and was in a similar situation, with an exposed area of 1½ acres (½ hectare), when the 6-inch OS map was published in 1906.

In 1907, however, the quarry was being worked (by whom, it has not been possible to establish), because the Wenlock Council received complaints from passers-by about the danger from blasting. The owners were not sending men on to the road to warn the public.[13]

By the early 1920s names could again be identified with the quarry. The first was the little-known Bonum Fertiliser Company, then J. Henshaw who also had quarrying interests at the nearby Knowle Quarry.[14]

From 1923 to 1933 the quarry was leased to Captain R.C.H. Kane.[15] Within a short space of time Kane was in trouble with the Council for not giving proper and efficient notice of blasting.[16] Also after Kane's arrival, the four running kilns to the south of the eastern aperture of the railway tunnel were in use. These lime kilns, which are still standing but in a ruinous state, were working until about 1930.[17] In fact, in this period, children living in neighbouring houses often used the kilns as a cooking medium by putting, for example, swedes 'won' from nearby fields to cook on top of the burning kilns. They also mischievously played with the narrow-gauge railway tubs on Sundays when the quarry was not being worked, often derailing them and then leaving them for irate quarrymen to rectify on Monday morning.[18]

Also in the time of Captain Kane, a large cylindrical steel running kiln was built. It was not thought that this kiln was very successful at the Plough, chiefly, it seems, because originally it was designed to be fired by gas rather than solid fuel. When Kane moved to the Westwood Quarry it was dismantled and re-erected there.[19]

Production of lime (the purest of which contained 90% calcium oxide) when Kane was the quarrymaster, ranged from 150 to 200 tons per week and most of it left the quarry in 8-ton-capacity sheeted

Capt R C H Kane, who gained his military rank during the First World
War, leased various quarries in the area.

The steel cylindrical kiln was erected in the Plough Quarry around 1925.

The stone crusher in the Plough Quarry around 1930.

railway trucks with 'Presthope Limeworks' displayed on their sides,[20] the rail spur from Presthope station having been relaid by this time. Also, Kane evidently had much more success in finding high calcium carbonate-yielding limestone than did Fields sixty years previously.

Kane closed the quarry in 1933 when the lease expired and it has not been worked since.[21]

In March 1938 it was offered for sale (presumably by the Lutwyche Estate) at the Gaskell Arms Hotel. The first bid was £300 and the quarry was withdrawn at £475.[22] It then remained dormant through-out the remainder of the decade and the Second World War years until 1952 when Markjohn Limespreaders became the occupiers.[23] This firm only used the quarry floor for parking and repairing facilities for its lime-spreading fleet which at that time was hauling lime out of the Coates Quarry.

By 1955 Pest Control Ltd was the new occupier, again only using the quarry floor to park its vehicles.[24] The next occupier was Harold Butler who used the quarry for similar purposes.

The quarry then became the home of a modern brick- and artifi-cial stone-making plant, built in 1965 by A.J. Mucklow & Sons Ltd. This company ceased production in 1980 and sold the plant to Eng-lish China Clays Ltd, who in turn ceased production in 1990. In 1992 the presses, and other equipment needed for the production of bricks and artificial stone, were stripped and removed, leaving only the factory shell. In 1994 English China Clays Ltd demerged its aggre-gates-quarrying activities, which resulted in the site being under the ownership of a company named CAMAS.

Apart from a towering quarry face to the south of the main road, the quarry now bears little resemblance to its original state.

A. & J. MUCKLOW & CO LIMITED
PRESTHOPE BRICKWORKS – MUCH WENLOCK
Telephone: Brockton 2161

References and Sources

1   1847 Tithe map
2   Microfilm 113, Shrewsbury Local Studies Library
3   Electoral Register, 1833
4   Wenlock Poor Rates Book, 1838
5   Wenlock Poor Rates Book, 1841
6   Tithe map
7   Wenlock Rates Books, 1855 and 1858
8   Much Wenlock & Craven Arms Railway Plan, 1860
9   Shropshire Records Office
10 Microfilm 109, Shrewsbury Local Studies Library
11 Microfilm 109
12 O.G. Mcdonald, Wenlock Council archivist, 1994
13 Wenlock Sanitary Book, 7.2.1907
14 A. Skutt, ex-quarryman, Westwood Quarry, 1973
15 R.C.H. Kane, quarrymaster, Plough Quarry, 1968
16 Wenlock Council Minute Book, 5.4.1923
17 H. Edwards, 1978
18 Edwards
19 G.H. Griffith, ex-quarryman, Westwood Quarry, 1987
20 Griffith
21 Kane
22 T.H. Thompson, scrapbook, Wenlock Archives
23 Wenlock Council Minute Book, 2.4.1952
24 D.L. Pardoe, engineer, A.J. Mucklow & Sons Ltd

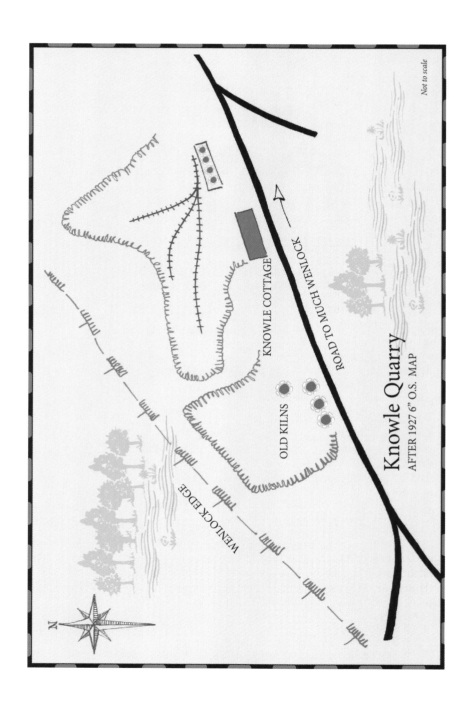

KNOWLE QUARRY 585977 This site was originally called Presthope Knowle Quarry and Limerock and was in existence in 1770.[1] It was some 70 years later, however, before names could be associated with the quarry. The first was probably Edward Rogers in 1838[2] and Edward Hayward in the years 1847–54[3] although the cottage attached to the quarry was occupied by Francis Price at that time. Both cottage and quarry were owned by the Earl of Bradford. The early workings were to the north-east of the cottage.[4]

Hayward was still quarrying in the 1870s, but apparently not very successfully. In fact it was suggested by the manager of the neighbouring Plough Quarry that Hayward's living 'was starvation itself'.[5]

In the 1880s, by which time Edward Hayward had been succeeded by Letitia Hayward, who had three sons and a grandson working for her,[6] the quarry was being worked to the south-west of the cottage.[7] There still exists a definite unworked area between the two workings. The kilns for the latter workings had their grates fronting on to the main road and were referred to in 1873 by Richard Hatfield, manager of Fields Mercantile Company.[8] In the 1960s the sunken remains of these kilns were just discernible.

In 1900 William Hayes and Son were the occupiers[9] and according to the six-inch OS map of 1902 the lime kilns to the north-east of the cottage were again in use, a tramway having been laid from the quarry face to the kiln bank.

In 1904 the inspector of mines and quarries noted a fatal accident at the Knowle when the quarry foreman (unnamed) fell from the quarry top whilst snaring rabbits.[10]

In 1911 Alfred Lucas Hayes (trading as William Hayes & Son) leased the quarry, known by then as Presthope Limeworks, from the Earl of Bradford for a period of 14 years. The rent was only £12 per annum plus 3d (1.25p) per ton as royalty on all limestone extracted. Perhaps the quite small rent and payments of royalty reflected the depressed state of the industry at that time. The terms of the lease were such that the lessee 'will work the demised stone and lime kilns in a proper and efficient manner and according to the best and most approved manner practised in similar undertakings in the district', also 'to keep books of account of stone and lime got with dates of production, with access by the lessor to the said books of account'.[11]

However, Hayes evidently did not complete the term of the lease, due perhaps to the Great War and the shortage of labour, because at the Gaskell Arm Hotel on 19 May 1919 George Newton, a builders' merchant of Gnosall, bought the quarry and cottage together with the lease to Hayes, from the Earl of Bradford's estate for £400.[12] From about this time J. Henshaw, from Shrewsbury, was blasting rock at the Knowle.[13]

Much like his quarrier neighbours, Henshaw appears to have been lax in his blasting operations because in 1921 the Council instructed the Town Clerk to write to Henshaw to request 'when future blasting is taking place men with red flags should be on the road'.[14]

Henshaw also utilised a pot kiln (which is still standing but in an advanced state of decay) in which to burn horseflesh, the horse carcasses from local knacker yards arriving just across the road at Presthope station. The bone dust, which was the residue after incineration, was sent to china and pottery works to whiten the clay. The kiln was called the 'bone kiln' and is situated to the south-west of the cottage. Poor lime sales at that time were the reason given for such an unusual use of this lime kiln.[15]

By 1927 the only kilns which appeared to be in use were near to the roadside and to the north-east of the cottage.[16] This kiln bank, which is still standing, contains four kilns, approximately five metres high and four metres in diameter at their tops. Also nearby is what appears to have been the quarry 'powder house' where explosives were stored, but was later converted to house livestock. If this was the explosive store, then the heavy, sealed, concrete roof has been replaced by a conventional tiled roof, probably to provide ventilation for livestock.

Quarrying finally ceased around 1927 when the quarry area was about three acres (1.2 hectares).[17] However, in the late twenties and

The old powder house in the Knowle Quarry was converted to house livestock.

early thirties Kane was using the kilns to burn stone from the Plough Quarry and as late as the Second World War the stables at the Knowle Cottage were used to house the horses which Kane employed in his Westwood Quarry.[18]

In 1945 the heirs of George Newton sold the now defunct Presthope limeworks to Bernard Scott Mason for £200,[19] the value probably being in the sturdily built limestone cottage.

The Knowle Quarry is managed by the National Trust, whose warden lives in Knowle Cottage. Because of its great geological and biological interest, especially the rich ground flora and the variety of trees to be found growing where quarrying activity once took place, it is now a Site of Special Scientific Interest (SSSI).[20]

References and Sources

1 Map of Westwood Common, 1770
2 Wenlock Rate Book, 1838
3 1847 Tithe map and Wenlock Rate Book, 1854
4 Tithe map and Wenlock Rate Book
5 Microfilm 109, Shrewsbury Local Studies Library
6 1881 Census
7 2½-inch OS map, 1889
8 Microfilm 109, op. cit.
9 *Kelly's Directory*, 1900
10 D.A. Holmes, thesis, Ironbridge Gorge Museum
11 V. Deacon, resident, Knowle Cottage, 1969
13 Borough of Wenlock Minute Book, 1919
14 Wenlock Council Minute Book, 1921
15 W. Harley, quarry lorry driver, 1969
16 6-inch OS map, 1927
17 H. Edwards, pre-1945 resident, Knowle Cottage, 1978
18 Edwards
19 Deacon
20 National Trust/Countryside Commission pamphlet

Contrasting views of the Lea Quarry in 2014.

LEA QUARRY 594984 The Lea was the most recent quarry to open and in terms of both size and production, the largest and most successful with upwards of 18 million tons of limestone extracted. Some of this volume, however, was at the expense initially of the peripheries of Westwood and Hayes quarries.

In 1841 Richard Milner, who was farming at the now demolished Lea Farm, appeared to have a passing interest in what the 1847 Tithe map discloses as a small quarry hole, near to the present quarry entrance.[1] But apart from Tom Norris (a successor to Milner at the Lea Farm) occasionally extracting stone between the wars, it was virtually a hundred years later before systematic quarrying commenced.

J. Cross and Sons Ltd were the first quarrymaster. The Cross company opened the quarry in 1943 for the express purpose of producing ground limestone to meet the demand for soil fertiliser.[2] A crushing and milling plant was installed but no lime kilns were built.

In 1947 around 180 to 200 tons of pulverised limestone was being produced weekly, but with peaks in the spring and autumn of upwards of 300 tons. This required the employment of nine quarry workers filling and pushing tramway tubs to the primary crusher.[3] Virtually the whole production after 1946 (which by the early 1950s included foundry stone) was transported from the quarry by the haulage firm of Hill & Mansell.

The Lea Farm was demolished to make way for the extension of the Lea Quarry.

The Lea Quarry in 1947 with Hill & Mansell's ex-WD lime spreaders
waiting to be loaded.

Work in the Lea Quarry c. 1950.

In 1948 a certificate to continue quarrying was renewed, with the proviso that the workings should not come within 30 yards of the footpath which follows the crest of the Edge.[4]

In 1957 J. Cross and Sons Ltd sold its interest in the Lea to the Ridge Limestone Company. By this time the exposed area of the quarry was five acres (2 hectares) and some 65 workers were employed producing and delivering around 1,000 tons of lime and limestone per week.[5]

Between 1959 and 1961 new processing machinery was installed which lifted production capacity to around 1,000 tons of lime and 3,000 tons of stone per week. Of the latter a small amount went for fluxing and, as fines, for brickmaking.[6] Also in 1961, the Ridge Limestone Company obtained new quarrying rights, providing the workings did not encroach within 50 feet of the highway.[7]

By 1968 production was in the region of 300,000 tons per annum (mostly roadstone) and in 1977 600,000 tons. The product breakdown then was: 80% aggregates, 10% crushed limestone for concrete products, 8% agricultural lime and 2% fluxing stone.[8] This compares with an output of all products in 1988 of 700,000 tons per annum, requiring the employment of around 20 quarrymen and the use of over 100 lorries working out of the quarry each day.[9]

To produce this quantity of limestone resulted in the expansion of the quarry to such proportions that by 1974 the exposed area was

Another farm which disappeared with quarry expansion on Wenlock Edge

25 acres (about 10 hectares)[10] and nearly double that area by the end of the '90s. To achieve this, the north-west workings of the Westwood Quarry and most of Hayes Quarry (as previously noted) were obliterated, including the gatehouse and at least one cottage which was situated equidistant between the main road and the crest of the Edge. Also, in the years 1973 and 1974 landslips occurred (clay layers between the limestone strata can be lubricated by water and thus allow large blocks of limestone to slip down-dip after quarrying has finished) necessitating the buttressing of the approximately 80-feet (25 metre) high quarry face which extends below the crest of the Edge.

Because of poor demand some quarrymen and senior staff were made redundant in 1992.

The original Lea Quarry, after over 50 years of continuous life, is now worked out; only the elaborate processing plant and offices remain on site. Extraction carried on taking place from what is now called Lea South. This is opposite to the original quarry, the stone being conveyed to the processing plant by way of a roadway driven under the main road. It was estimated that the reserves of limestone would last until 2042 but the quarry closed in 2007.[11]

Established in March 2011, Edge Renewables moved into Lea Quarry North the following year. They are a renewable energy business which uses woodchip and biomass fuels.

The Lea Quarry in its heyday c. 1989.

Preparations for blasting at Lea Quarry in 1989.

Overburden removal at Lea South in 1992.

An aerial view of Lea Quarry before work had begun on Lea Quarry South.

Gazetteer of Limestone Working Sites

References and Sources

1   Wenlock Rate Book, 1841
2   Wenlock Council Minute Book, 29.9.1943
3   G. Chegwen, general manager, Ridge Limestone Company, 1974
4   Wenlock Council Minute Book, 5.2.1948
5   Chegwen
6   Chegwen
7   Wenlock Council Minute Book, 5.10.1961
8   Much Wenlock Museum
9   W.S. Hughes, foreman, Lea Quarry, 1988
10 Chegwen
11 *Shropshire Star*, 7.1.1994

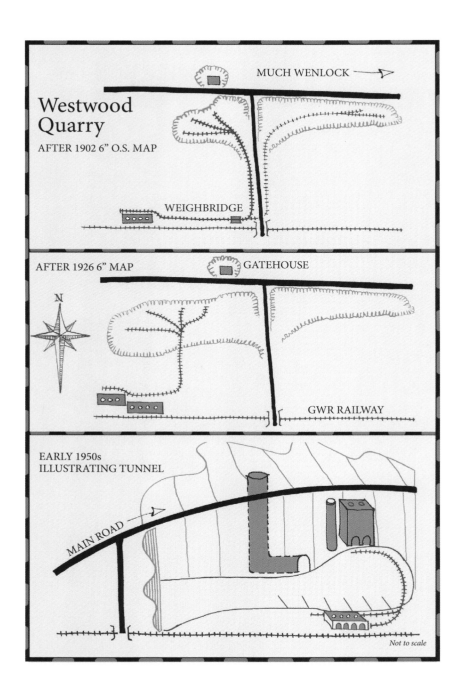

Westwood
Quarry
AFTER 1902 6" O.S. MAP

MUCH WENLOCK ➤

WEIGHBRIDGE

AFTER 1926 6" MAP

GATEHOUSE

N

GWR RAILWAY

EARLY 1950s
ILLUSTRATING TUNNEL

MAIN ROAD ➤

Not to scale

WESTWOOD QUARRY 598986 Lime-burning was taking place in the region of this quarry in 1714 when Isaack Anns Phillips and Arther Jones's 'widdow' were each paying 10/- (50p) per annum rent to the Manor of Wenlock for lime kilns, and Edward Gorton (also at that time associated with Hilltop Quarry) was paying 30/- (£1.50) rent for a similar activity.[1]

Most of Stretton Westwood was common land until 1808 when the local Commissioners for the enclosing of Westwood Common made the first allotment of land 'for the purpose of furnishing stone and other materials for the making of roads'.[2]

In 1833 quarrying was taking place, on what was common land, between the Much Wenlock–Church Stretton road and the crest of Wenlock Edge.[3]

By 1838 John Robinson and the brothers John and Richard Roberts were paying the Wynnstay Estate for 'lymerock' won from somewhere in the vicinity of Westwood Quarry.[4]

In 1847 a small quarry was being worked immediately on the left when turning off the main road down the lane leading to Bourton Westwood.[5] This quarry was probably being worked by George Shepherd, a farmer and lime-burner of Westwood Cottage Farm, who in the years 1851–2 produced 114 tons of lime.[6]

By 1863 Edmund Raby had taken over part of the quarry north of the Bourton Westwood lane and near to where the railway later came. The landowner was Lord Wenlock.[7] Raby was joined at the same time by Thomas Jukes who was quarrying south of the lane, on Lord Forester's land.[8]

A year later Anstice, the well-known ironmaster (on behalf of the Madeley Wood Company), agreed to pay Lord Wenlock £3,500 for 35 acres of limestone-bearing land situated where the Westwood Quarry is now.[9] This could well explain why the *Wellington Journal* of 21 December 1864, in connection with the recently opened railway to Presthope, made the comment: 'Upwards of 200 men will be employed, principally for the extraction of fluxing stone, at these two quarries.' The other quarry was Lilleshall.

By 1865 sidings had been laid from the newly opened railway, Lord Wenlock agreeing to pay the Wenlock Railway Company £400 towards the cost of £1,200. In return he would not be required to pay loading dues.[10] It was around this time too, that the now derelict kiln bank alongside the old railway track was constructed.

In 1873 the Madeley Wood Company sent 9,000 tons of limestone to its Blists Hill foundry. Originally (prior to late 1865) the stone went by rail to Buildwas, then downriver by barge before transhipment again, this time on to a horse tramway. The cost of haulage was 3/- (15p) per ton of which 1/6 (7½p) was accounted for by the river section. However, a saving of 1/- (5p) per ton was made after the rail spur across the river from Buildwas was opened in late 1865.[11]

A weighing machine of 1870, similar to the one used at the Westwood
Quarry.

The Madeley Wood Company was still at Westwood in 1878,[12] but
by the 1890s George Lloyd appears to have been the quarrymaster. In fact, at this time the quarry was better known as 'Lloyd's
Quarry'.[13] The workings still extended to both sides of the Bourton
Westwood lane but with the major workings to the north-east, with
tramways from both locations to the kilns near the railway.[14] In this
period too, a weighbridge existed (somewhere in the vicinity of Bourton Westwood lane) from which weighed limestone was transported
by horse and cart to the railway sidings below.[15]

Before 1900 Lloyd went into partnership with Alfred Kendrick and
from then onwards the quarry became better known as Westwood
Quarry.[16]

According to the 6-inch OS map of 1902 the emphasis of working
then was to the north-west of the Bourton Westwood lane and like
some other quarries at that time it could have been a hazard to the
public as it was unfenced.[17]

Around 1905 Lloyd sold out to Kendrick. The latter then entered
into a partnership with a personage by the name of Shaw.[18] This partnership was supplying lime to the gasworks in 1913[19] and roadstone to
the Council (to repair Callaughton Ash) in 1918.[20] It was around this
time too, that German prisoners of war were employed in the quarry.[21]

Sometime between 1919 and 1920 Moore & Shields (the latter
having only one leg after being wounded in the Great War) became
the quarrymasters and by then the quarry was better known as the

TELEGRAMS: " MUCH WENLOCK."

TELEPHONE: 23, MUCH WENLOCK

FROM **MOORE & SHIELDS,**

WESTWOOD QUARRIES,

PROPRIETOR
C. F. SHIELDS.

MUCH WENLOCK,

193

WENLOCK
HYDRAULIC
BUILDING LIME.

AGRICULTURAL LIME.

PLASTERING LIME.

FLUXING STONE for
Blast Furnaces,
Foundries, etc.

GROTTO, ROCKERY,
and BUILDING STONE.

ROAD STONE
(Machine or Hand Broken)
all sizes from ¼-in. upwards.

CHIPPINGS for
Top Dressing Footpaths,
Carriage Drives, etc.

LIMESTONE GRIT
for Poultry.

CRAZY PAVING.

'Knowle Limeworks'. By 1926 Moore & Shields had increased the size of the kiln bank by a further three kilns and had constructed a more direct tramway from the north-west workings.[22] The north-east workings had by that time become, and have since remained, derelict.

With the expansion of the workings, a cottage which existed to the south of the main road was demolished to make way for further limestone extraction.[23] Moore & Shields also extended quarrying in the late twenties to the north-west of the main road. But in the first instance only the top crinoidal band of rock (known to quarrymen as 'gingerbread') was extracted; this was because of its good fluxing properties, limestone for foundries being in greater demand then than for other uses.[24] At busy times in this period upwards of 20 railway trucks of fluxing stone were despatched each day from Presthope station to Black Country iron foundries and to the Lilleshall Ironworks. The Lilleshall Quarry, it will be recalled, was closed by this time. Lorry drivers then were being paid 5d (2½p) per ton (two-ton lorry loads) for loading their lorries by hand and taking the stone to Presthope station.[25]

Notwithstanding the apparent brisk, but spasmodic, trade in supplying limestone to local iron foundries, C.F. Shields, who lived with his wife and family in the now demolished gatehouse (toll) bungalow, found trade difficult. Although a great variety of stone products were being sold (a billhead of the firm discloses that building lime, roadstone, fluxing stone, agricultural lime, plastering lime, chippings, poultry grit and stone for crazy paving were being marketed) this was a time of general economic depression and it was not an easy task to keep the concern viable. To quote C.F. Shields' son, 'My father was glad to see the back of it.'[26] In fact, trade in the twenties was so poor quarry owners asked the Council to consider using more limestone for local road repairs. The Council surveyor said limestone was not much good for surfacing, but he would try some on Station Road and St Mary's Lane.[27]

Despite poor trade, Shields showed some appreciation of his quarry workers' efforts by hosting a dinner for them at the Horse & Jockey on New Year's Day 1926. Forty sat down to dinner; the toast to Moore and Shields was proposed by H. Price Esquire, with Captain Shields replying.[28]

In 1933 Captain C.R.H. Kane bought the quarry and shortly afterwards moved the steel cylindrical kiln from the Plough Quarry. It was erected by two of his workmen (Garbett and Pearce) just southeast of the main road, virtually opposite where the gatehouse once stood. This kiln (which proved not very efficient, largely because it had to be reduced in height to suit the new location),[29] together with two conventionally built running kilns, were charged (each of approximately 80-tons capacity) at road level and discharged on the level of the quarry floor, from whence the burnt lime was either

The steel kiln at Westwood Quarry erected c. 1935.

Westwood Quarry: conventional running kilns built around 1935.

loaded directly on to road vehicles or taken by tramway tub to the railway sidings for transhipment. For the latter exercise, because of the falling gradient from the kiln grates to the sidings, a brakeman or 'spragger' was needed.[30]

Whilst Kane was the quarrymaster a considerable amount of limestone was extracted from the north-west side of the quarry above the main road. It was here in 1936 that Albert Skutt lost his eyesight in a blasting accident. Kane had also constructed at the farthermost end of these workings a small kiln bank containing three pot kilns served by a single adit. This kiln bank was built in 1938 and demolished (because of the extension of the Lea Quarry) in the late 1970s. Also in the immediate Second World War period, a shaft was sunk from the workings above the main road which connected to a tunnel just south-west of the steel kiln that had been bored under the road from earlier workings. This shaft and tunnel was intended to increase the ease and speed of transporting stone both to the lime kilns near the railway and also for use (in pulverised form) in a small plant near the kilns where building blocks were made and where limestone was milled for ground lime.[31] This innovation, however, was never put into use. The shaft has long since been obliterated by the extended workings of the Lea Quarry, whilst the tunnel aperture (just recognisable) is waterlogged.

In the early fifties Kane offered to supply stone, at cost plus free transport, to repair Henmore Hill lane. However, because Kane's

lorries constituted around 80% of the traffic on the lane, the Council did not consider the gesture too generous.[32]

Captain Kane continued working Westwood Quarry until he sold it to the Ridge Limestone Company in 1954. At the height of productivity Kane was employing between 25 and 30 men to produce around 25,000 tons of lime and stone per annum.[33] Most of the production left the quarry by road but there were also about three railway trucks leaving weekly with lime.[34]

When Ridge Limestone gained control of the quarry it ceased to extract limestone (despite permission being obtained to install a crushing and screening plant in 1956)[35] but continued to utilise the lime kilns for a further four or five years, the charges coming either from its Coates or Lea Quarries. Burnt lime production by then was only around 800 tons annually, with coke being used instead of coal for a while, but this proved inefficient.[36]

After the railway was closed in 1962, the sidings alongside the kiln bank were lifted. The kilns became derelict and by 1968 the area was occupied by a company called Wenlock Stone and Concrete Products Ltd. The three running kilns near the main road are still standing (just!) but are in an advanced and dangerous state of decay. Incidentally, it was the lime kilns at this quarry which resulted in Wenlock

In this 1965 picture of the Westwood Quarry, the kiln adit can be seen to the right, the steel kiln is hidden in foliage in the centre and there is a tunnel entrance further left in the picture.

Derelict kiln bank and railway loading wharf at Westwood Quarry in 1965.

having its one and only air raid during the last war. This was on the night of 25 July 1940.[37] The flames from the open kiln tops could be seen at night from the air; this attracted a German aircraft which dropped two bombs (without doing any damage) by the kilns near the railway.

The workings to the north-west of the main road have been completely obliterated by the Lea Quarry workings, whilst the quarry floor south-east of the main road was used in part as a refuse tip for Wenlock in the early 1960s and later as a scrapyard and vehicle storage area by a local garage proprietor.

References and Sources

1   Manor of Wenlock Survey, 1714, National Library of Wales
2   Shropshire Records Office (Westwood Common)
3   1-inch OS map, 1833
4   Wenlock Rate Book, 1838
5   1847 Tithe map
6   Summers/Adney/Brookes Railway Survey, 1852
7   *Kelly's Directory*, 1863
8   Much Wenlock & Craven Arms Railway Plan, 1860
9   SRO (Lord Wenlock)
10 SRO (Lord Wenlock)
11 Microfilm 109, Shrewsbury Local Studies Library

12 Wenlock Council Minute Book, 1878
13 F. Preece, Westwood resident, 1968
14 2½-inch OS map, 1889
15 Preece
16 Preece and *Kelly's Directory*, 1900
17 Wenlock Sanitary Book, 27.12.1900
18 F. Stretton, ex-clerk, Shadwell Quarry, 1968
19 Wenlock Council Minute Book, 16.2.1913
20 Wenlock Council Minute Book, 7.2.1918
21 G. Walters Snr, ex-quarryman, 1968 and G.D. Cooke, ex-quarryman, 1986
22 6-inch OS map, 1926
23 W. Harley, quarry lorry driver, 1969
24 G.H. Griffith, ex-quarryman, Westwood Quarry, 1986
25 Harley
26 C.F. Shields Jnr, 1968
27 *Shrewsbury Chronicle*, 3.4.1925
28 T.H. Thompson, scrapbook, Wenlock Archives
29 Cooke
30 M. Pearce, 1985
31 Griffith
32 Wenlock Council Minute Book, 6.9.1951 and 11.11.1952
33 C.R.H. Kane, quarry owner, 1968
34 K. Jones, railway historian, 1991
35 Wenlock Council Minute Book, 6.12.1956
36 G. Chegwen, manager, Ridge Limestone Company, 1974
37 Thompson

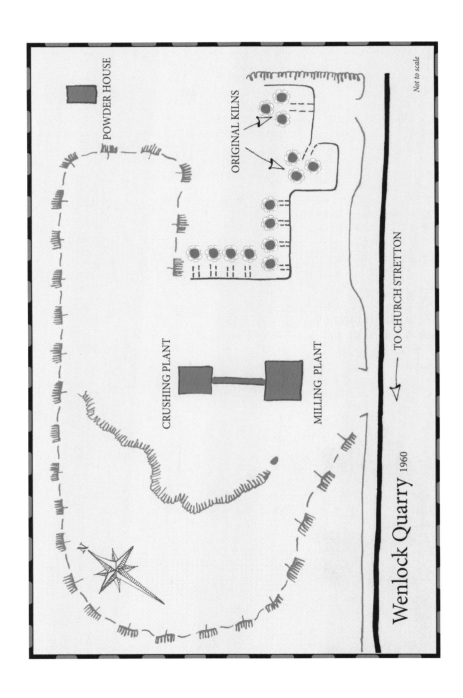

POWDER HOUSE

ORIGINAL KILNS

CRUSHING PLANT

MILLING PLANT

Not to scale

TO CHURCH STRETTON

Wenlock Quarry 1960

WENLOCK (or HAYES) QUARRY 602992 The name of this quarry rather depended on the date when it was referred to. Until 1926 it was known as Oakleys' Quarry.[1] From 1926 it became Cox's Rock[2] and, latterly, Hayes Quarry. To add confusion, to some of Hayes' workers, especially when the company was working Shadwell Quarry, it was called Wenlock Quarry.

Much like the Lea Quarry, this site was one of the last to have been opened, although as far back as 1889 a small quarry hole did exist, but this was only a few metres in area and appeared not have been worked.[3]

It was not until after the Great War that quarrying commenced in earnest. This was in 1923 when the first kilns were built and the brothers Frederick, John, Edwin and William Oakley were the quarriers, for in that year they leased the quarry from the owner, George Lloyd, for five years. The rent was £22 5s 0d (£22.25) per annum plus royalties of 6d (2½p) per ton for burnt lime and 4d (1½p) per ton of limestone produced.[4] The area of the quarry and reserves was 7½ acres (3 hectares) in extent.[5]

It appears that the Oakleys' occupation of the quarry was shorter than the lease stipulated (at the time John Oakley was complaining about the falling off in the lime trade)[6] because in March 1926 the quarry was bought from the estate of George Lloyd by Gladys Cox (a relative of A. James Cox, one-time managing director of William Hayes & Son Ltd) for £250.[7] Prior to this the executors of George

The remains of the quarriers' cabin and kiln bank at Wenlock Quarry.
They were built c. 1920.

Lloyd's estate had put the quarry up for auction at the Gaskell Arms Hotel, but failed to find a buyer.[8]

From 1926, when William Hayes & Son Ltd commenced operations, until production finally ceased in 1964, when the quarry was sold to A. J. Mucklow & Sons Ltd, it was worked continuously by the former concern. A possible reason for Mucklow acquiring the quarry was to use the stone in the manufacture of bricks at the Plough. However, there is no evidence of this having taken place.

Another kiln bank was built in 1929. This comprised six kilns served by two adits.[9] These kilns, which are still standing but filled in, are situated near the roadside and near the Coates Quarry boundary.

In 1935 limeburning facilities were again increased, when another kiln bank was built. This newer kiln bank, which joined on to the original one, contained eight kilns, much the same size as the first ones, some seven metres in height and three to four metres in diameter at their tops, but each one had its own adit. Tom Fothergill, the quarry foreman and chief lime-burner at the time, said: '25 cwt of good limestone produced one ton of lime from these kilns.'[10] However, some of the kilns were never put into use; indeed, a few were not even lined with firebricks.[11] About this time too, a small loading platform was built together with a small mill (to grind burnt lime) and a storage shed. From this platform both lump lime straight from the kilns (transported by tramway) and milled lime could be loaded directly on to lorries on the roadside.

Until well into the 1950s, tramways were used extensively in this quarry, the tubs carrying limestone to the kiln bank being hauled

The kiln bank at Wenlock Quarry built about 1935.

A derelict mill hopper at Wenlock Quarry in 1965.

by horse. During this period also, the stone for burning had to be reduced in size manually, the men at the quarry face wielding sledge-hammers to break the stone into acceptable sizes. The manpower then was eight to ten quarrymen.

In 1953 William Hayes applied to Wenlock Council to extend the quarry, so allowing production to increase to between 12,000 and 14,000 tons per annum.[12]

In addition to producing calcium oxide, Hayes Ltd sold a considerable amount of stone for foundry needs. Its principal customer was the Round Oak Steelworks in Brierley Hill. This trade, however, had lapsed by the early fifties. It was in this decade too, that due to the high cost of fuel, the production of burnt lime ceased and a jaw crusher and a five-ton-per-hour hammer mill was installed to produce ground lime.[13]

For the remainder of the quarry's life all limestone extracted was crushed and ground for soil fertiliser. At peak production in the late fifties and early sixties, some 15,000 tons were produced per annum, spring and autumn being the busy times with the quarry virtually idle during the winter months. The manpower by the 1960s was seven to eight men, motor dumpers and excavators having replaced the tramway tubs.[14] Apart from Hayes' own vehicle, the principal hauliers and limespreaders were J. Hatcher and Hill & Mansell. There were no weighing facilities on site, which meant that all production had first

The weighing steelyard in the railway goods yard used by Hayes for produce from the Wenlock Quarry.

to be transported to the weighbridge on the coal wharfage in Wenlock (this weighbridge survived until 1992) before eventual delivery.

The quarry was not worked after 1964, the remaining reserves of stone being absorbed by the extension of the Lea Quarry workings in the late 1970s, which also accounted for the demolition of the crushing and milling plants and part of the newer kiln bank. The part of the quarry floor nearest to the road was used as a lorry park for hauliers hired to transport paving slabs and bricks from the Coates and Plough Quarry plants. However, with the demise of the paving-slab- and brick-making, this part was no longer used.

References and Sources

1 W. Everall, auctioneer, Shrewsbury, 3.11.1924
2 T.H. Thompson, scrapbook, Wenlock Archives
3 2½-inch OS map, 1889
4 Shropshire Records Office
5 Everall
6 Thompson
7 Shropshire Records Office
8 Everall
9 Date over kiln adit
10 Thompson and *Daily Sketch*, 1.4.1935
11 D. Watkins, foreman, Wm. Hayes & Son Ltd, 1965
12 Wenlock Council Minute Book, 5.3.1953
13 Watkins
14 S. Edwards, lorry driver, Wm. Hayes & Son Ltd, 1966

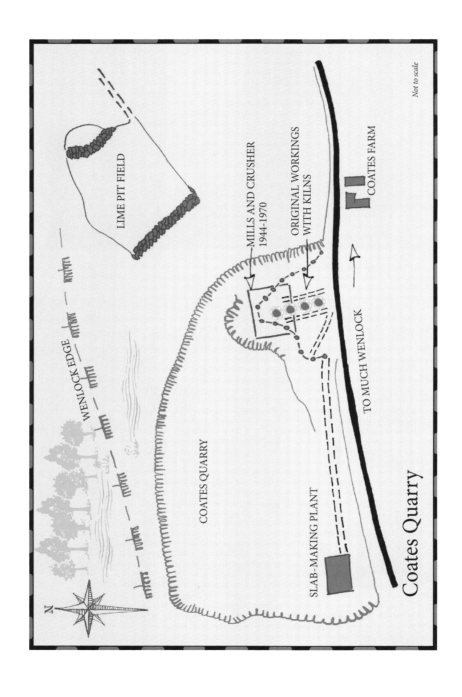

COATES (or COTES) QUARRY 604994 Quarrying was taking place in the immediate vicinity of this site before the enclosure of Westwood Common in 1806–7; for in 1770 there existed Lime Pit Field which was situated a few metres north-east of the present quarry entrance at map reference 605995.[1]

It was not until 1841, however, that people could be identified with this location. By that time Thomas Hotchkiss was renting Lime Pit Field, together with lime kilns, from Lord Forester.[2] Seven years on and William Jukes was the quarrier, his rent being £5 5s 0d (£5.25) per half-year.[3] It was from this quarry in 1857 that Jukes was selling lime to the gasworks in Barrow Street for 10/6 (52½p) per cartload.[4]

According to the Tithe map of 1847, there existed a small disused quarry together with waste heaps a few metres to the north-west of the Coates near the crest of the Edge, but there are no references to the present quarry until 1851–2 when Thomas Jukes (who was also farming at the Coates Farm and was later well known as a talented 'tilter' at the local Olympian Games)[5] was the quarrier. In these years he produced 159 tons of lime.[6]

The *Wellington Journal* of 22 May 1869 reported that Richard Thomas of Hughley was found burnt to death in the lime kilns at the Coates. It appears he had been drinking at the Horse & Jockey the previous evening and had left late in a state of intoxication!

By 1888 *Porter's Directory* records that William Reynolds was the farmer and lime burner at the Coates. Also by the following year it appears that quarrying at the original Lime Pit field had ceased.[7]

A late 1950s photograph of the Coates Quarry, owned by Ridge Limestone Ltd, at the height of its production.

By the 1890s George Meakin had succeeded Reynolds. Meakin's chief customer at the time was Lord Forester, for whom he was producing lime for fertiliser and mortar.[8] Meakin was still at the Coates in 1907, for in that year he successfully tendered to supply road-stone, at 3/9 (18.75p) per ton, to repair Homer road.[9]

By 1910 George Lloyd was the quarrymaster.[10] The quarry was still quite small but five lime kilns had been built.[11]

By 1914 Edwin (Ted or 'Mallet') Sankey was the quarrier, in which capacity he remained until 1936.[12] At one period, 1922–7, Sankey was paying George Lloyd (and after 1924 the latter's estate) a rent of £10 per annum plus royalties of 6d (2½p) and 4d (1½p) per ton for all lime and limestone produced.[13] Presumably, Lloyd had bought the quarry from Lord Forester by that time.

On 3 November 1924 the executors of George Lloyd's estate put the quarry (which by that time had only three kilns and was known as Coates Limeworks) up for sale.[14] It has not become clear who the purchasers, if any, were.

After perusal of the six-inch OS maps of 1902 and 1926, it seems that neither Lloyd nor Sankey produced a great deal of limestone, as between these dates the exposed area of the quarry remained virtually unchanged. However, some of Sankey's meagre production was transported to Wenlock railway station for delivery further afield. To do this he kept a pair of horses, which were stabled at his home in Sheinton Street.[15]

After Sankey, Captain Kane of Westwood Quarry took over the Coates with, by that time, its six kilns and was burning lime there in the early years of the Second World War. And after the air raid scare at Westwood Quarry, the kiln tops had to be covered at night. This was done by horses pulling corrugated iron frames over the exposed kiln tops.[16]

In order to meet demand for agricultural lime (brought about by the need to produce more home-grown food at the time) the Halkyne Mining Company took over the quarry in 1944. A modern crushing and milling plant was installed and all traces of the lime kilns, and the tramways feeding them, disappeared.[17]

In 1945 a consortium headed by Peddigrew, Jones and Horner became the quarriers. Production was around 1,200 tons of ground limestone (the sole product) per week in peak periods and about 20 men (some on night shift) were employed in the quarry.[18] Most of the lime at that time was hauled out of the quarry and spread on farmland by the transport firm Markjohn Spreaders.

Much like the Halkyne Company, Peddigrew, Jones and Horner must have had a very short stay at the Coates because it is recorded in the Borough of Wenlock receipt book that the Ridge Limestone Company was also quarrying there in 1945.

Photographed in August 1960, Bill Whitfield was driving Jemson's
newly delivered yellow lorry to collect lime from the Coates Quarry for
agricultural use.

By 1955 this latter concern had increased production to over
70,000 tons of lime per annum.[19] Trade was brisk in the 1950s with
the quarry being worked day and night seven days a week, which
brought complaints from nearby residents protesting about the
noise, particularly blasting at weekends.[20]

The Ridge Limestone Company ceased production at the Coates
in 1963, by which time the exposed area of the quarry was five acres
(two hectares) and output had increased to over 100,000 tons annually. The chief haulage and spreading contractor by that time was
Evan Jemson Ltd.[21] Because of the road haulage licensing laws
appertaining in this period quarry owners, if not using their own
transport, tended to rely on one or two haulage contractors only.

Although the quarry had been worked out, the processing plant
was still used for the production of lime for a further two years, raw
material being transported from the company's Lea Quarry to be
dried and milled.[22]

By 1970 the whole quarry had become derelict with all the machinery either having been dismantled or demolished and by 1972 the
quarry entrance had been partially landscaped with coniferous trees.
This coincided with the south-west end of the quarry floor being utilised by A. J. Mucklow & Sons Ltd as a site for a paving slab manufacturing plant. Incidentally, when site preparation for this plant was
taking place, upwards of 30 lb of decaying nitroglycerine was found

Evan Jemson Ltd were the main contractors at the Coates Quarry in the 1960s.

down an old blasting bore hole. At the time, workmen did not realise what the semi-liquid plastic material was that they were shovelling. An explosives company representative could not safely take it away, so it was smothered with neutraliser *in situ*.[23] This plant and the approximate 80-foot (25 metre) quarry face (which in 1972 was subjected to a landslip) are not visible from the main road.

Apart from the remains of a water filtration and pumping plant near the roadside, there is little indication now that this was an important quarry.

Today Grange Fencing operate a storage facility from this quarry. Also Lime Green Products, manufacturing hydraulic lime mortar, lime plaster and lime render for use on historic buildings and ecological developments, started operating here in 2002. Sadly they do not use any local products.

References and Sources

1   Map of Westwood Common, 1770
2   Wenlock Poor Rate Book, 12.5.1841
3   Forester Estate Book, 1842
4   Much Wenlock Gas Company Account Book
5   T.H. Thompson, scrapbook, Wenlock archives
6   Summers/Adney/Brookes Railway Survey, 1852
7   2½-inch OS map, 1889
8   F. Preece, resident, Stretton Westwood, 1968
9   Wenlock Sanitary Book, 1.8.1907
10 F. Stretton, ex-clerk, Shadwell Quarry, 1968
11 6-inch OS map, 1902
12 T. Langford, ex-quarryman, 1964
13 Shropshire Records Office
14 W. Everall, auctioneer, Shrewsbury, 3.11.1924
15 G.D. Cooke, ex-quarryman, 1986
16 G.H. Griffith, ex-quarryman, 1986
17 J. Ryle, ex-quarryman, 1973
18 G. Brown, foreman, Ridge Limestone Company, 1974
19 Borough of Wenlock official guide, 1955
20 Wenlock Council Minute Book, 2.9.1954
21 G. Chegwen, general manager, Ridge Limestone Company, 1974
22 T. Joyce, foreman, Ridge Limestone Company, 1968
23 D.L. Pardoe, engineer, A.J. Mucklow & Sons Ltd, 1972

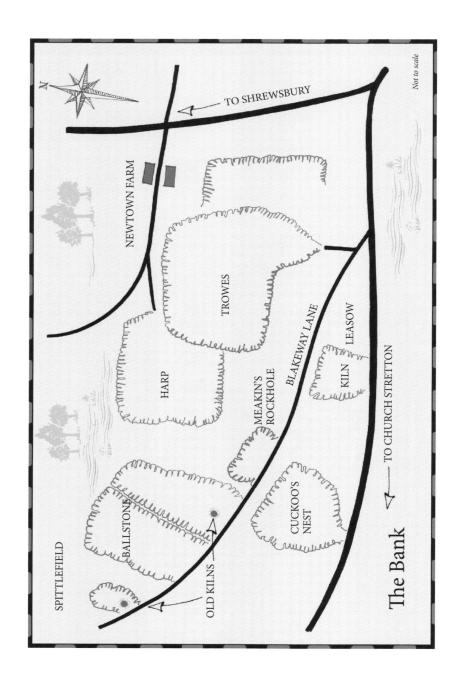

CUCKOO'S NEST QUARRY 612996 The first evidence of quarrying at this site was in 1841 when Jeremiah Cooper was renting the quarry and lime kilns from Lord Forester.[1]

By 1848 the quarrier was Thomas Jukes,[2] most probably the same person who was connected with the neighbouring Coates Quarry. Thomas Jukes was mentioned by various sources between 1842 and 1900 as a quarrier and lime-burner and even as a lime merchant.[3] Exact locations and specific years, however, have been difficult to establish, but possibly he may have been interested in this site and the Coates at the same time.

Also in 1848, George Adney (a local dignitary who was concerned with, amongst other things, the coming of the railway and the building of the gasworks) was the owner and occupier of a small quarry directly alongside and to the north-east of the brick-built house which stands in front of the Cuckoo's Nest.[4] Incidentally, this house was once the Forester's Arms and later the Last, the publican being a shoemaker of the name of Haynes.[5] This inn was so called because it was the last public house before leaving the town.[6]

Jukes' and Adney's workings eventually merged and then the whole quarry extended from the main road to Blakeway Lane. In fact there is an obvious cart track from the quarry to Blakeway Lane.

In 1881 Elijah Nicklin was both farming and in possession of a 'limeworks' at the Cuckoo's Nest.[7] It was probably from this quarry too that Elijah's relative John Nicklin was delivering lime in 1856 to the gasworks.[8]

According to the 2½-inch OS map of 1889, the quarry with attendant kilns was still active, but since that date little is known except that Aaron Lloyd was probably the last person to work the quarry before it was completely transformed by him (and later his son Jack) into a farmstead around the turn of the century, when a Dutch barn and other farm buildings were erected on the quarry floor. The only evidence now of past quarrying activities is a rather shallow rock face. The last remaining pot kiln and the original farm buildings were demolished in the 1970s. Newer farm buildings were built on the quarry floor in the late eighties.

References and Sources

1   Wenlock Poor Rates Book, 12.5.1841
2   1847 Tithe map
3   Wenlock Council Minute Book, 1.11.1889
4   1847 Tithe map
5   S. Mullins, curator, Wenlock Museum
6   T.H. Thompson, scrapbook, Wenlock Archives
7   1881 Census, Shrewsbury Local Studies Library
8   Much Wenlock Gas Company Account Book

KILN LEASOW (meaning Kiln Enclosure) 615996 Little is known about this site, save that it was one of the earlier quarries to have been worked in this vicinity. The reason for this was probably ease of accessibility of the limestone to the main road, the town and the cottages and crofts which were clustered on and around the Bank.

It has not been possible to establish either when quarrying commenced or when precisely it terminated. However, it is possible that Elizabeth Edwards may have been interested in limestone there in 1836[1] and George Edwards between 1838[2] and 1844.[3]

By 1848 quarrying had ceased and George Edwards, who by that time was the landlord of the nearby Limeman's Arms, seems to have been more interested in the site as pasture.[4]

It is unlikely that this quarry has been worked since before the middle of the nineteenth century.

In the 1930s and '40s the site was known as Mona Cliff (as indeed was a small bakery which was situated in the cottages opposite to the quarry entrance) but it has not been possible to establish how this name came about.

In the 1970s the remains of at least six pot kilns could just be distinguished from surrounding spoil heaps. These were really only small mounds, sunken at their centres and on the side where the grate was situated. These were obliterated by the earthworks required to make a car park for the National Trust. The only remaining feature suggesting that this site was once a quarry is a shallow limestone face near to Blakeway Lane.

References and Sources

1   D.A. Holmes, thesis, Ironbridge Gorge Museum
2   Wenlock Rates Book, 1838
3   Holmes
4   1847 Tithe map

THE BANK This is the area of land, on the dip slope of the Edge, stretching west from the A458 road to Shrewsbury and to the north of the Blakeway Hollow Lane and was more commonly known in the eighteenth century as 'New Towne'. Within this area there is evidence of extensive old quarry workings. However, quarrying on the Bank seems to have been undertaken not by large concerns but rather by one-man enterprises or by people who were jointly lime-burners and crofters, farmers, cow-keepers or even beer-sellers! Also, the quarry faces are shallow, suggesting that they were worked in a primitive way and in most cases many years ago.

BALLSTONE QUARRY 610997 This site was known originally as Lower Spittlefield[1] and, towards the end of its life, as the Bonnetts Quarry.[2] This latter name obviously originated from the Bonnetts houses which preceded Havelock Crescent.

This quarry is probably the oldest on the Bank, dating back certainly to 1714 when the personages of George Simons and Edward Southerne were paying a yearly rent of 10/- (50p) and 16/- (80p) respectively to the Manor of Wenlock for the right to extract and burn limestone.[3]

Francis Southerne, in the year of his death in 1730, was also a 'lymemaker' on Spittlefield. His 'tooles' from his 'lymeworks' were valued at only £3. He was a farmer/limeman and, as previously noted, was heavily in debt when he died, suggesting perhaps that neither farming nor limeburning was very profitable at that point in time.[4]

By 1785 Thomas Trowe was in Spittlefield and he was paying £6 per year rent which included a house and stable.[5]

No other references occur until 1839 when Spittlefield, extending to six acres (2½ hectares) and still containing valuable limestone, was occupied by George Roper and put up for sale by Lord Forester. The sale took place at the White Hart Inn in Wenlock.[6] The new proprietor was probably Humphrey Hinton who owned a quarry and lime kilns in this vicinity in 1841.[7] Nine years later, however, John Reynolds of Newtown Farm was the quarrier.[8] Reynolds also had possession of a smaller quarry alongside and to the west of Spittlefield, at the entrance to which a pot kiln in a ruinous state can still be seen.

Also in 1848 Quarry Piece, immediately to the east of Spittlefield, was being worked by Edward Harrington,[9] from which in the years 1851–2 he produced 166 tons of lime.[10] Harrington was in his seventies at the time, but fortunately he had a son working with him.[11] The Harringtons were still at the quarry in 1858.[12]

In the latter half of the last century the two sites appeared to have merged, and henceforth became known as the Ballstone Quarry (because of the abundance of ballstone, especially in Quarry Piece).

According to the 2½-inch OS map of 1889 the lower part of the Ballstone appeared to have been in a state of disuse. However, before 1900 John Nicklin and Jeremiah Cooper were in partnership at the quarry.[13] Thereafter, and certainly until 1916, Aaron Lloyd (who, it will be recalled, was also at the Cuckoo's Nest at that time) was the quarrymaster.[14] Whilst at the Ballstone Lloyd burnt a considerable amount of limestone for mortar, and this product was, towards the end of his occupancy, transported to his customers by his son Joseph (later to become a farmer and a respected alderman of the town). Also it was Lloyd who supplied most of the stone for the building of the Lady Forester Hospital.[15] Some years later in 1913 he won an order from the Council to supply 200 tons of roadstone[16] and in the following year was supplying lime to the gasworks.[17]

There is no evidence to suggest that the Ballstone Quarry was worked between the Great War and 1938, when the firm of Moles Brothers recommenced working the east part of the quarry. By 1940, however, they had abandoned the site, leaving as the only evidence of their occupancy a concrete block which had been used as a base for a piece of machinery.[18] It was in this period, too, that a fatal accident occurred when Harold Firmstone was killed whilst involved in carrying explosives in the quarry.[19] After Firmstone's death, Fred (Buller) Sankey worked the quarry alone! However, this was only for a few months.[20]

It has been suggested that since the Second World War, Jack Corfield, who lived in Yew Cottage, burnt limestone at the Ballstone; but it must be concluded that such quarrying and limeburning as did occur was only on a very small scale. Two pot kilns (served by a single adit) can still be seen near the entrance to the east part of the quarry. Also, just discernible are the remains of other banks of pot kilns and at the entrance to the west part of the quarry a small building still stands. This appears to have been a stable, probably to house horses required for both working in the quarry and for transporting products further afield.

Save for these latter three small excursions into quarrying, the site has not been worked for approaching 100 years.

References and Sources

1   Manor of Wenlock Survey, 1714, National Library of Wales
2   T.H. Thompson, scrapbook, Wenlock Archives
3   Manor of Wenlock Survey
4   S. Mullins, curator, Wenlock Museum, 1981
5   Wenlock Estates Rent Book, 1785
6   Forester box, Shropshire Records Office
7   Wenlock Poor Rates Book, 12.5.1841
8   1847 Tithe map
9   1847 Tithe map
10 Summers/Adney/Brookes Railway Survey, 1852
11 1851 Census
12 Wenlock Council Rate Book, 1858
13 D.A. Holmes, thesis, Ironbridge Gorge Museum
14 D. Watkins, 1969, and *Wildings Directory*, 1916
15 Watkins
16 Wenlock Council Minute Book, 4.12.1913
17 Wenlock Council Minute Book, 2.4.1914
18 G. Brown, foreman, Ridge Limestone Company, 1974
19 G.D. Cooke, ex-quarryman, 1986
20 Cooke

MEAKIN'S ROCKHOLE 612997 Immediately to the east of the Ballstone Quarry is a very small quarry hole (the floor of which is often waterlogged and a recipient of refuse) which verges on to Blakeway Lane.

Very little is known about this site save that it does not appear to have had any kilns and that evidently George Meakin (hence the name of the site), who, it will be recalled, had associations with the Coates Quarry, was winning limestone from around this spot just prior to the First World War.[1] Thereafter it appears to have been abandoned.

References and Sources

1   *Kelly's Directory*, 1913, and A. Skutt, ex-quarryman, 1973

TROWE'S QUARRY 613999 The first person to be identified as a quarrier and lime-burner at this location was Thomas Trowe, who in the years 1785–9 would probably have been found working that part of the Bank now known as the Plantation.[1] It was some 11 acres (4½ hectares) in extent (including the rough pasture field to the south of the Plantation, where traces of sunken pot kilns and spoil heaps can be seen) and without doubt the largest quarry on the Bank.

By 1835 Thomas Trowe (or perhaps, due to the lapse in time, his son) was better known as a beer-seller on the Bank.[2] Possibly Trowe was combining two occupations at the time. In any case, by 1838 he had been succeeded by John Hailey.[3] Hailey, who had a croft joining on to the turnpike road near to where the Horse & Jockey pub used to be, was also quarrying at a point immediately east of Trowe's Quarry in 1848[4] and was still there in 1851.[5]

It has not been possible to identify any later quarriers (if any) with this location.

The remains of pot kilns (only just distinguishable from surrounding spoil heaps, but with firebricks evident) still exist in Trowe's, but judging from the advanced tree growth, it would be reasonable to assume that this quarry, together with the one to the east, had ceased to have been worked well before the end of the nineteenth century.

References and Sources

1   Wynnstay box, National Library of Wales, and *The Universal British Directory*, 1789
2   *Pigot's Directory*, 1835
3   Wenlock Rate Book, 1838
4   1847 Tithe map
5   1851 Census, Shrewsbury Local Studies Library

HARP QUARRY 613001 This quarry, some four acres (1.7 hectares) in extent, can be found immediately north-west of Trowe's Quarry, and when it was being worked, access was through Newtown Farm.

It has not been possible to establish when quarrying first started, but the site was certainly being worked by 1833 when Thomas Harrington (a well-known Methodist and a founding trustee of the Methodist Chapel in King Street) was the quarrier.[1] In the period 1851–2 he produced 450 tons of lime, a considerable amount at that time.[2] The following year his rent to Lord Forester was £14 per half-year.[3]

Who the last quarrier was, and when, it has not been possible to determine, but Harrington appears still to have been at the Harp in 1871.[4] After perusal of the 1881–2 6-inch OS map, it is questionable if the quarry was still being worked at that time.

Today the site is marked by the sunken remains of three banks of lime kilns, each of three-pot kilns, and an example of how a quarry face had been utilised as a wall for a lean-to building.

One other point of interest: by virtue of its name the quarry could possibly have had a connection with the Harp Inn (built in 1650 and demolished in 1938 to make way for the widening of the Gaskell corner) which once stood at the south-west end of the High Street in Much Wenlock.[5]

This quarry face at the Harp Quarry was used as the wall for a lean-to building since gone.

References and Sources

1   Electoral Register, 1833
2   Summers/Adney/Brookes Railway Survey, 1852
3   Forester Estate Gathering Roll, 1853
4   *Kelly's Directory*, 1871
5   T.H. Thompson, scrapbook, Wenlock Archives

STOKES BARN BANK QUARRY 612001 At this site limestone was burnt both to the east and west of Stokes Barn, sunken kilns and traces of burnt lime being in evidence.

The first person to be identified with quarrying here was Richard Beck (or Peck) of Harley, who in 1778 was paying £4 rent for lime kilns in Edgefield. The kilns were to hold no more than three wagonloads, of 55 bushels each load.[1] The adjacent quarry (to the north-west) was called Edgefield, and Beck could possibly have been quarrying there too, but because the latter's kilns were at the foot of the scarp slope, probably Beck was more concerned with the western part of Stokes Barn Bank.

Isaac Shepherd, an ironmaster of Garmston, near Leighton, was probably the next person to win limestone from this site. In previous years he was interested in neighbouring Edgefield, but by 1838 his attention had turned to Stokes Barn Bank.[2]

By 1848 George Shepherd (who also had connections with the early workings of Westwood Quarry) had succeeded him.[3]

Also in 1848, the bank of kilns to the east of Stokes Barn could have been in possession of Thomas Harrington, whose Harp Quarry was only a few metres away[4] and where stone for the kilns may have been quarried, as there is little evidence of major extraction having taken place near these kilns.

Although various names have been associated with lime-burning in this vicinity, it is more than likely that John Reynolds of nearby Newtown Farm was there in the early 1850s, when in a two-year period he produced 141 tons of lime.[5]

The last reference to this quarry was in 1884 when John Norry was there. It is unlikely that quarrying or lime-burning has taken place much later than this date.

References and Sources

1   Wenlock Estates Rent Book, 1778
2   Wenlock Rate Book, 1838
3   1847 Tithe map
4   1847 Tithe map
5   Summers/Adney/Brookes Railway Survey, 1852

EDGEFIELD QUARRY 608001 Unlike the other quarries situated north of Blakeway Lane, Edgefield (and its neighbour, Smokey Hole Quarry) is not strictly on the Bank, but rather on the crest of the Edge.

The first reference to Edgefield (save for a possible connection with Beck, referred to at Stokes Barn Bank) was in 1801. Then the famous engineer Thomas Telford was interested in the site. Telford, with partners, leased the Red House lime kilns from Sir William Pountney of Middlesex.[1] The Red House (also marked on early maps as the New Works) is the house (originally two cottages) standing at the foot of the scarp slope of Wenlock Edge, on the right-hand bend when descending Harley Hill.

Also in the same year, with partner John Simpson, Telford entered into an agreement for the procurement of limestone with the Lords Barnard and Bradford.[2] The limestone was carried by trucks, by way of an inclined plane, from Edgefield Quarry on the crest, to the kilns at the base of the scarp slope.

An inclined plane of the period was described thus: a simple piece of machinery at the top, composed of a barrel and friction wheel, and the road laid with iron rails; two ropes being fastened to the barrel and connected to the wagons top and bottom; the greater weight of the load descending, brings up the inferior from the bottom, working up and down two sets of iron rails alternatively.[3] The braking system was rather primitive, consisting of a wooden pole, called a 'jig', and operated by a brakeman or 'jigger' perched on the descending and accelerating wagon – a rather precarious occupation.[4]

The remains of the inclined plane was visible when approaching Harley Hill from the direction of Shrewsbury (a parallel line of trees ascending the scarp slope) and where, until recently, a partly buried L-section plateway or tramplate was *in situ* on the kiln bank side of the Blakeway Farm road.

The need for this inclined plane (on older maps called the Jenny Wind probably after the name 'jinney', meaning plateway) was twofold; because the stone at the base of the scarp slope was shale (Wenlock shale) and also to alleviate the need, particularly if the lime and stone was being transported to the north, to negotiate Harley Hill. This presupposes the Harley Hill road, in anything like its present form and condition, existed then, which is unlikely, as it was not realigned until 1812,[5] and also not many years earlier the Sheinton road from Wenlock to Shrewsbury was turnpiked because the route was being used in preference to Harley Hill, which was in such a deplorable state.[6] In fact the condition of Sheinton road was suspect too. Mossenden Carter, the surveyor, wrote in 1724: 'Teams from the lime kilns come over our road and throw up rowts and stones.'[7]

In 1822 Isaac Shepherd, the Leighton ironmaster, became the operator of the kilns, inclined plane and quarry above. Apart from

In this photograph, the track of the inclined plane can be seen going up
Wenlock Edge.

paying rent to what appears to be the new owner, William Harvey,
Earl of Darlington, Shepherd was required to pay 2d (0.8p) per ton
royalty on all limestone extracted, allow his books of account to be
inspected, install a weigh machine and pay additional rent of 10/-
(50p) per annum for the use of the inclined plane.[8] At that time
weighing machines were relatively expensive to install and maintain. A 13-foot (4 metre) x 7-foot (2 metre) machine with a cast-iron
plate would have cost £87 in 1826.[9]

The quarry appears still to have been working in 1841 when
Edward Griffith, a limemaker from Homer, was there.[10] However, in
the same year he was succeeded by George Stephens.[11] Thereafter no
further references occur, and according to the 6-inch OS map of 1882
the quarry had by that date fallen into disuse (the last quarrier leaving some fine ballstone faces) and appears to have remained so ever
since.

Two other points of interest about this quarry: unlike similar
undertakings on Wenlock Edge, the workings progressed down the
dip slope as opposed to upwards towards the crest; and this is the
only site where the Edge has been deliberately breached (albeit
insignificantly) by quarrying activities.

Near the bottom of Harley Hill the remains of the kiln bank can
still be seen.

References and Sources

1 2495/Box 71, Shropshire Records Office
2 Much Wenlock Museum
3 B. Trinder, *The Industrial Revolution in Shropshire* (Chichester, Phillimore, 1973)
4 R.K. Morris, *Railways of Shropshire* (Shrewsbury, Shropshire Books, 1991)
5 J.G. Bramwell, *A Short History of Cressage* (Cressage, Bramwell, 1984)
6 Trinder
7 L.C. Lloyd, '18th Century Administration of Shropshire'
8 2495/Box 71
9 J. Copeland, *Roads and Their Traffic 1750–1850* (Newton Abbot, David & Charles, 1968)
10 Wenlock Council Rate Book, 1841
11 Wenlock Poor Rate Book, 1841

SMOKEY HOLE BANK 611002 This site is alongside and to the north-east of Edgefield, to a point just beyond the A458 road. In fact, the road appears to divide the quarry, with evidence of very limited workings immediately alongside and to the north-east of the road.

It has not been possible to establish when quarrying commenced, but John Reynolds of Newtown Farm, would probably have been found lime-burning there in 1841[1] and certainly by 1848.[2]

By 1851 Miss Elizabeth Edwards (who had had connections with the Kiln Leasow Quarry 15 years previously) was the quarrier, and was paying the Wynnstay Estate a rent amounting to £5 15s 0d (£5.75) per annum.[3] Even by mid-nineteenth-century standards, the hewing of rock would not have been a very common occupation for a spinster. Nevertheless, with the help of two quarrymen[4] she produced 256 tons of lime in the years 1851–2.[5] Miss Edwards appeared to have still been at Smokey Hole in 1861.[6] Her lime kilns then were possibly the ones fronting on to the south-west side of the main road. According to the 1847 Tithe map, these kilns were built after the 1840s.

By 1871 quarrying had been abandoned and the whole area of some 3½ acres (1½ hectares) had been planted with trees.[7]

Apart from quarry faces, the only remains of quarrying now are two pot kilns, with a large lump of congealed burnt lime nearby, in the wood at map reference 609002, traces of CaO and coal on the scarp slope, and a kiln, with firebricks still visible, fronting on to the main road. Incidentally, this latter lime kiln, together with other obliterated ones which were alongside it, may have given this quarry its name, as the smoking kiln tops would have been easily visible to passers-by on the main road.

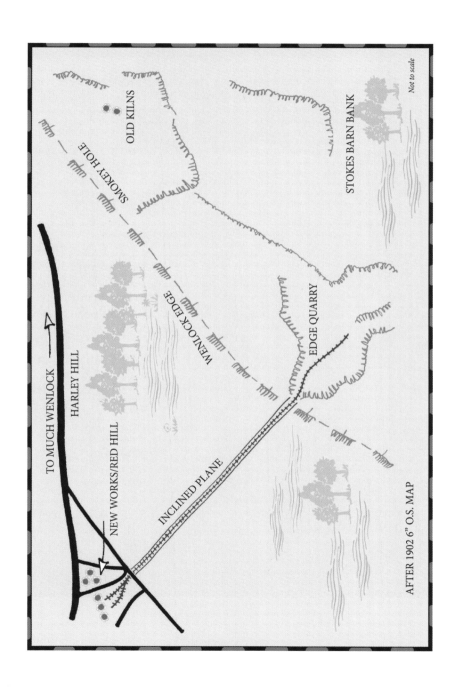

OLD KILNS

SMOKEY HOLE

STOKES BARN BANK

WENLOCK EDGE

EDGE QUARRY

TO MUCH WENLOCK

HARLEY HILL

NEW WORKS/RED HILL

INCLINED PLANE

AFTER 1902 6" O.S. MAP

Not to scale

The plantation stone at Smokey Hole Quarry with enhancement to make the writing legible. It is thought these stones recorded the date when the area was replanted with trees.

No early records of Smokey Hole exist, but it could have been that the original road leading from Newtown Farm led to fields, woodlands and Smokey Hole only. If this were the case, and Smokey Hole was being worked at the time, then it would not be unreasonable to assume that when Harley Hill was realigned in 1812, all that was needed was to breach the quarry face. Close inspection of the quarry faces either side of the road suggest that this may have happened!

References and Sources

1   Wenlock Poor Rate Book, 1841
2   1847 Tithe map
3   1851 Census
4   1851 Census
5   Summers/Adney/Brookes Railway Survey, 1852
6   *Harrod & Co.'s Directory*, 1861
7   Plantation stone, 1871

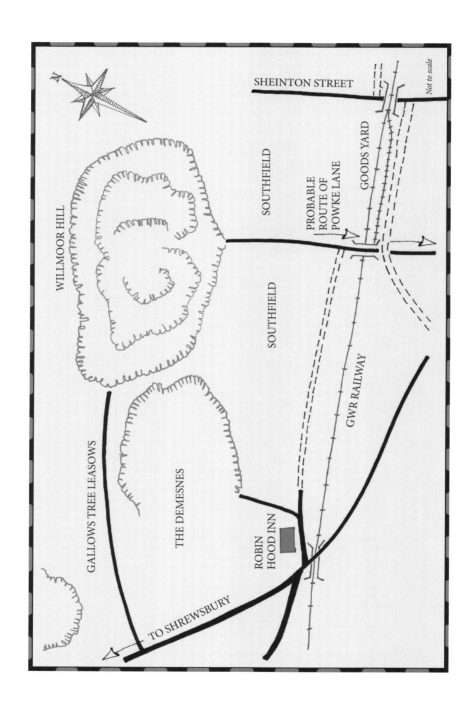

GALLOWS TREE LEASOWS and SHEEPWALK 613003 A small amount of quarrying has taken place between the lower part of Gallows Tree Leasows and the Sheepwalk, but exactly when and by whom it has not been possible to determine. All that can be said is that according to the tithe map of 1847 a quarry did not exist in this vicinity, but by 1889 the 2½-inch OS map of the latter date discloses that a quarry with lime kilns had not only been established but also had been abandoned.

In recent years the quarry hole has been planted with coniferous trees.

THE DEMESNES QUARRY 618001 This is another site about which very little is known save that it did not appear to have been in existence in 1848,[1] but had been worked and abandoned by 1881,[2] leaving traces of calcium oxide in the surrounding soil, suggesting that lime kilns sometime had been *in situ*.

A theory was expressed by an elderly resident (long since deceased) that the limestone and lime required in the construction of the railway buildings and bridge abutments around 1862 could have originated from this area.[3] Although unproven, this is not improbable as the site, like its neighbour Willmoor, was only worked for a limited period around the time the railway was being built, with a Charles Cooper being active in the Demesnes in the early 1860s.[4]

The quarry's output seems to have been transported down a roadway (or tramway?) to the Shrewsbury road. The route ran alongside and to the north-east of the now defunct Robin Hood Inn.

The area is now rough land covered with bushes and stunted trees.

References and Sources

1   1847 Tithe map
2   6-inch OS map, 1881
3   T. Hewlett, 1964
4   Much Wenlock and Craven Arms Railway Plan, 1860, Shropshire Records Office

WILLMOOR HILL QUARRY 618002 Another old quarry about which little is known save that it may have been worked by a T.H. Wellings who was paying the Wynnstay Estate rent for a 'limerock' in this vicinity in 1841.[1] However, there was no evidence of quarrying in 1848,[2] but it may have been worked again prior to 1889 when it was designated as disused with old lime kilns.[3]

Access seems to have been both from the south-east of the site, by way of what is now Bridge Road, but at that time, from Mardol Lane, then by way of Powk Lane through 'South Field'; and from the west from Newtown Farm.[4]

Willmoor Hill could arguably have been another location from which material was won for use in the building of the railway. Limestone would have been easily accessible for the engine shed and goods yard buildings and the Sheinton Street bridge. The whole site is now covered with coniferous trees, but in the Second World War years it was completely bare and a Royal Observer Corps observation post (used to track and report allied and enemy aircraft) was situated at its highest point.

References and Sources

1   Wenlock Poor Rate Book, 1841
2   1847 Tithe map
3   2½-inch OS map, 1889
4   2½-inch OS map

SYTCHE QUARRY 620006 Extensive quarrying has taken place in the area of rough land and woodland known as Sytche Coppice. This coppice, in various stages of tree growth, stretches north-east from the Sytche House to near the Homer road.

On the 1833 OS map the area of land where the hospital now stands was designated as a limeworks and in the years 1822–44 Edward Arlington (or possibly Harrington) would probably have been found quarrying there[1] and for which in 1838 he was paying the Wynnstay Estate £4-a-year rent.[2]

According to the 1847 Tithe map, most of the Sytche was called the Sheepwalk, suggesting perhaps that by that date most of the area had ceased being worked and had been given over to rough grazing. Nevertheless, there is an area of land (some four acres or about 1½ hectares in extent) just below where the reservoir is situated, which was known as the Rock Field. At this location there are pot kilns, in a very derelict state and can only just be distinguished from surrounding spoil heaps. It was from here possibly that George Shepherd (who, it will be recalled, had quarrying interests elsewhere at that time) was winning limestone in the years 1851–5.[3] Long after the demise of the quarry, these lime kilns were used as a depository for still-born calves from a nearby dairy herd, especially when frost made it difficult to bury the carcasses.[4]

By 1872 quarrying had probably ceased, for in that year the area was planted with trees.[5]

The small quarry where the Sytche House stands had been worked and termed 'disused' by 1848.[6] The occupier of the buildings then was Edmund Mason, who a few years later could have been found working the Standhill Rock Quarry. In 1862 it was described as a 'croft and old quarry'. It is extremely unlikely that this part of the Sytche was worked after the middle of the nineteenth century.

References and Sources

1   D.A. Holmes, thesis, Ironbridge Gorge Museum
2   Wenlock Council Rate Book, 1838
3   Wenlock Council Rate Book, 1851–6
4   J.F. Langford, farmworker, 1970
5   Plantation stone, Sytche Coppice
6   1847 Tithe map

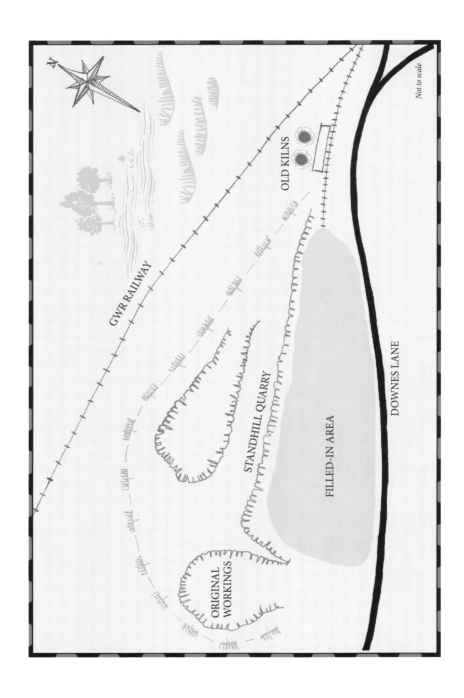

STANDHILL ROCK QUARRY 626004 It has been suggested that building stone used in the construction of the 'Great Church' and other prominent and important buildings in Wenlock came from here or nearby Shadwell Quarry, the limestone then being better known as Shropshire Marble.[1] Be that as it may, it is much, much later before firm evidence emerges of quarrying taking place at this location. This was in 1833 when Joseph Norry was quarrying in the vicinity.[2]

In 1839 Murchison, the eminent geologist, described Standhill Rock as a massive reef-knoll.[3]

By 1841 T.H. Wellings (who also had quarrying interests on Willmoor Hill) was renting the quarry and lime kilns from Sir Watkin Williams Wynn.[4] Seven years later William (or Richard) Roper had taken over the tenancy. The site was quite small and the entrance was from the south.[5]

By 1850 Edmund Mason was also limemaking at Standhill Rock.[6] Perhaps his workings were to the north of the site where much more activity has taken place. Because the railway did not exist at that time, this part of the quarry may have been physically linked to Shadwell Quarry, the railway eventually separating the two. Wherever, Mason made 114 tons of lime in the years 1851–2, whilst Roper's production was only 41 tons.[7] Incidentally, Mason was also the landlord of the Punchbowl Inn in the Bullring.[8]

A typical limestone tub.

These pot kilns at Standhill Quarry date from c. 1865.

In anticipation of the railway passing near, Sir Watkin Williams Wynn, on behalf of the Wynnstay Estate, arranged in 1861 for a siding to be laid into the quarry.[9] This took place some twelve months later.

The year 1864 saw the South Wales and Cannock Chase Coal and Coke Company as the quarrymaster.[10] Like some other limestone concerns at the time, the SW & CCC & C Co. was initially frustrated in its attempt to sell economically fluxing stone to the east Shropshire iron foundries because the rail spur from Buildwas to Coalbrookdale and beyond had not been completed. After November 1865, when the link was made, trade improved somewhat.[11] Production in 1873 reached 25,000 tons per annum (which included a contribution from Shadwell), 90% of which went for fluxing.[12]

In 1880 the workforce was seven or eight quarrymen under the foremanship of George Sankey of Homer. The quarry manager was T. Onions and later (1885) J.H. Ritson.[13]

The SW & CCC & C Co. was still leasing the quarry in 1887, but it was not being operated,[14] perhaps reflecting poor trading conditions prevailing at the time.

At the end of 1887 the Town Council proposed that Standhill Quarry (situated in Downes Lane) be used as a rubbish tip, which eventually it became.[15]

The rail sidings had been lifted by 1903.[16]

As late as 1924, F.W. Yates, who farmed the Brookhouse Farm, was spasmodically quarrying and burning limestone (at the farthest point from the refuse tip) for use on his farm. This was pursued in a very small way indeed, his farmworkers extracting the stone and looking after the kilns.[17] Evidently agricultural tenants were allowed to get and burn stone for their own use;[18] presumably this was when a quarry could not be let.

Two rather derelict pot kilns can be seen alongside what was the rail siding wharf, and also two ballstone faces, where traces of explosive bore holes are visible. However, most of the quarry was filled in with refuse during the first half of the twentieth century.

References and Sources

1   A. Clifton-Taylor, *The Pattern of English Building* (London, Batsford, 1972)
2   Electoral Register, 1833
3   R. Murchison, *The Silurian System* (London, John Murray, 1839)
4   Wenlock Rate Book, 12.5.1841
5   1847 Tithe map
6   *Slater's and National Commercial Directory*, 1850
7   Summers/Adney/Brookes Railway Survey, 1852
8   *Kelly's Directory*, 1856
9   Microfilm 113, Shrewsbury Local Studies Library
10 *Wellington Journal*, 1864
11 Microfilm 113
12 Microfilm 113
13 *Kelly's Directory*, 1879 and 1885
14 Wenlock Sanitary Book, 30.12.1887
15 Wenlock Sanitary Book
16 6-inch OS map, 1903
17 E. Evans, 1968
18 Box 1224/2/531, Shropshire Records Office

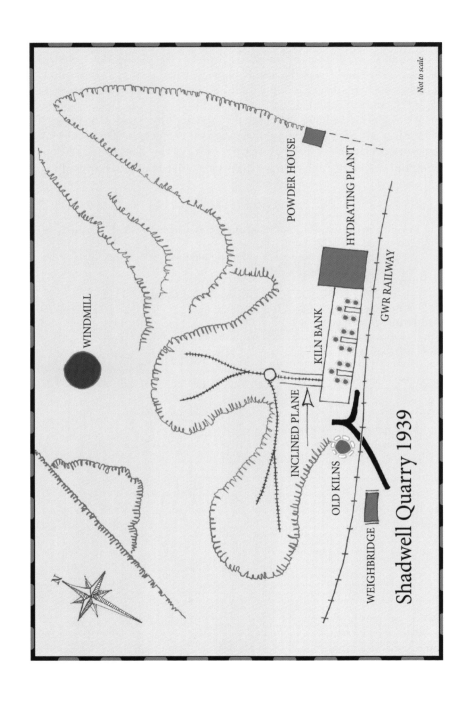

Not to scale

POWDER HOUSE

HYDRATING PLANT

GWR RAILWAY

KILN BANK

WINDMILL

INCLINED PLANE

OLD KILNS

WEIGHBRIDGE

Shadwell Quarry 1939

N

SHADWELL or SHADY WELL QUARRY 626006 Much like its
neighbour, Standhill Rock, Shadwell's history is probably longer
than can be supported by solid evidence.

Charles Sankey is the first recorded quarrier to have had an interest in limestone in this vicinity. This was in 1833.[1]

In 1849 Francis and John Yates took a 14-year lease on a new
quarry in Windmill Field, later called Shadwell Rock. They expected
to produce 9,000 tons of limestone per annum.[2]

In the years 1854–8 George Shepherd (who seemed to be a prolific
quarrier in the district at that time) was also interested in Shadwell
limestone.[3] Probably the Yates family (by virtue of the name of their
location) were more interested in the northern part of Shadwell,
whilst Shepherd's activities were possibly nearer Downes Lane. Notwithstanding their 14-year lease, there is no evidence to suggest that
the Yates family were at Shadwell after 1858.[4]

It was in the early 1860s, however, before the quarry came into
prominence. This was when the South Wales and Cannock Chase
Coal and Coke Company became the operator.

In 1862 rail sidings were laid to the quarry from the Buildwas
to Wenlock line and in the same year a siding was sanctioned from
Buildwas station to the riverside to allow fluxing stone from Shadwell
to be sent down the Severn to the Madeley Wood Company's ironworks.[5] In 1864 100 tons was sent via this route at a cost of £5 for
rail carriage.[6] After 1865, when the rail spur across the river to Coalbrookdale was opened, trade picked up. In 1873 22,500 tons of fluxing stone was despatched to the Black Country.[7]

By 1889 a large kiln bank had been constructed adjacent to some
earlier pot kilns.[8]

In 1896 the SW & CCC & C Co. enlarged its explosive magazine
(powder house).[9] For this to happen presumably trade was still con-
tinuing to improve.

The SW & CCC & C Co. continued to work the quarry until 1910,[10]
the last manager probably being Benjamin Beech.[11] When operations
ceased, about a dozen men were employed and virtually all the production left the quarry by rail in the company's own eight-ton trucks.[12]

By 1912 the quarry was in the hands of M.A. Boswell, a builder
and contractor from Wolverhampton.[13] However, between 1912 and
1925 there does not seem to have been much activity at Shadwell,
nor indeed between 1925 (by which time Tarslag Ltd was the occupier) and 1932.[14]

Although Tarslag was still at Shadwell in 1939,[15] it was in the
same year the Shadwell Quarry Company unsuccessfully applied to
the Wenlock Council for permission to widen the Bullring.[16] Still in
the same year (November) the Econo-Lime Products Company was
at Shadwell.[17] This concern's stay was short-lived too, because the

quarry lay idle throughout most of the Second World War years, with only a watchman employed. The rail sidings had been lifted by this time.

Immediately after the war, Lime Applications Ltd acquired Shadwell. This company had a wooden bungalow built alongside the weighbridge which was situated on the Downes Lane side of the railway. The certificate to renew quarrying in 1948 forbade working on Windmill Hill as the windmill was to be preserved![18]

Lime Applications, apart from burning lime (some of the limestone for which was transported from Farley Quarry) produced hydrated lime for the building industry. In the years 1946–8 weekly production was some 200–300 tons with an additional ground lime output of up to 500 tons in peak periods. The workforce to accomplish this was around a dozen men.[19] In those days too, it was a common sight to see ex-army four- and six-wheel-drive trucks (converted for use as limespreaders) roaring up the Bullring from Shadwell Quarry before negotiating Wilmore Street and the High Street. In this period also, complaints were received by the Town Council about the state of Abbey Bank in Downes Lane.[20] And the Council itself asked Lime Applications on various occasions to help with the cost of repairing the Bullring caused by the excessive use of the road by its limespreaders.[21] Blasting caused the Council concern as well, with stones falling off the Priory being attributed to blasting shake from Shadwell.[22]

In this period also an accident occurred in a kiln adit. Whilst quarryman Derek (Nainny) Langford was drawing lime from a kiln grate at the far end of an adit, a grate near to the aperture collapsed, allowing burning lime to partially block the entrance; Langford was burnt running to safety.

In the early 1950s William Hayes & Son Ltd (of the Wenlock Quarry) took over the running of Shadwell. This concern ceased production of burnt lime but continued to produce ground lime for fertiliser, six to eight men being employed to produce an average of about 400 tons per week using a diesel-powered primary crusher and mill. By this time too, motor dumpers had replaced the tramways and the hydrating plant had been dismantled and sold for scrap.[23]

Due principally to the lack of accessible high calcium carbonate-bearing rock (there was quite a lot of 'bluestone' with a low calcium content, which in the days of limeburning particularly, ran and congealed in the kiln rather than calcined; and also mudstone was quite common) the Hayes Company ceased production in 1956.[24] After this date the processing plant, storage hoppers, bungalow and weighbridge were dismantled.

For the next ten years Shadwell lay idle again (the Abbey Estate making safe the perimeter fence and lime kilns) until February 1966 when Wrekin Carriers Ltd became the quarrier.[25] This company, which

The Shadwell Quarry in a derelict state in 1960.

produced roadstone and hardcore only, installed a modern stone-crushing plant, storage hoppers and a new weighbridge. The former two of these were situated near where the kiln bank once stood, the kilns having been completely obliterated. Unlike previous operators, who used the Bullring for access, Wrekin Carriers drove an access road through from the north-east of the site (the Farley Road end). The extraction technique changed too, inasmuch as the quarrying took place deeper into the dip slope, resulting in more of a gallery system being employed, with bench heights of approximately 15 metres.

It was this concern which transferred a considerable amount of spoil to the north-east of the disused railway track, thus creating a sizable hillock overlooking Downes Mill.

In 1978 Steetley Construction Materials Ltd became the quarrier. This company installed a new crushing plant of greater capacity in 1980, thus increasing production potential. Also, with Steetley's considerably increased production, the area and depth of the quarry was increased dramatically, resulting in parts of the quarry floor being covered with an excessive amount of water when the water table was high.

A minor blasting accident occurred in 1981 when rocks fell on the nearby William Brookes School, slightly injuring three pupils and damaging classroom roofs.

In the 1990s Shadwell was now one of only two quarries being worked in the locality. In 1989 production was around 350,000 tons

Shadwell Quarry showing the gallery system of quarrying.

per annum, all of which was used as aggregates in various sizes from six inch (150 mm) to fines and dust. To achieve this output eight quarrymen were employed, supplemented by a further twelve personnel in the transportation of the stone and in administration. The lack of good calcium carbonate-bearing reserves did not justify the installation of a lime milling plant.[26]

A later quarry operator was Redland Aggregates, who in 1994 estimated the Shadwell had a remaining life of about seven years; however the quarry closed in 1996.[27] Since then there have been several failed attempts to create a business in this quarry.

References and Sources

1 Electoral Register, 1833
2 DD/WY/5370, Clwyd RO
3 Wenlock Rate Books, 1854–8
4 Wenlock Rate Books, 1858
5 Microfilm 113, Shrewsbury Local Studies Library
6 Microfilm 113
7 Microfilm 113
8 2½-inch OS map, 1889
9 Wenlock Council Minute Book, 1896
10 F. Stretton, clerk, Shadwell pre-1914, 1968
11 *Kelly's Directory*, 1900
12 Stretton

13 Wenlock Council Minute Book, 1912
14 Wenlock Council Minute Book, 1925 and 1932
15 *Shrewsbury Chronicle*, 2.6.1939
16 Wenlock Council Minute Book, 1939
17 Wenlock Council Minute Book, 1939
18 Wenlock Council Minute Book, 1948
19 W. Pitcher, ex-quarryman, 1973
20 Wenlock Council Minute Book, 1952
21 Wenlock Council Minute Book, 1949 and 1951
22 Wenlock Council Minute Book, 1951
23 D. Watkins, foreman, Wm. Hayes & Son Ltd, 1975
24 Watkins
25 Wenlock Council Minute Book, 1966
26 V. Russell, manager, Steetley Construction Ltd, 1989
27 *Shropshire Star*, 7.1.1994

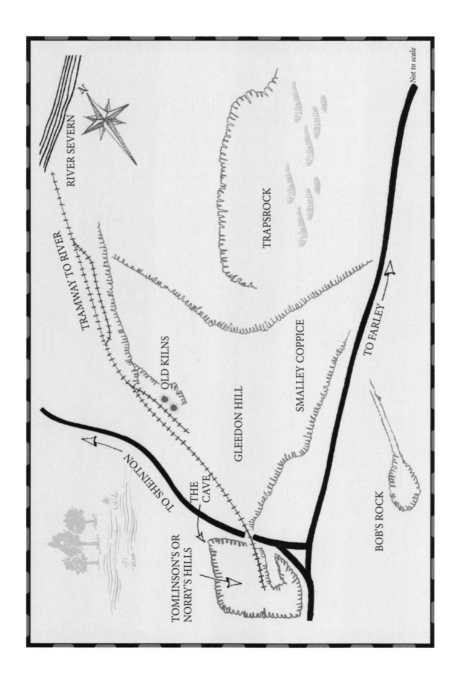

TOMLINS (or TOMLINSON'S) HILLS QUARRY 624013 This site, which has been extensively worked over the years, may originally have been known as Nutgrove Hill, where as early as 1714 Richard Dawley was lime-burning and, by the standards of the time, in quite a big way.[1] The later name of Tomlins, however, probably originated from a William Tomlins of Homer, who in March 1745 acquired 'a parcel of limerocks' known as Stone Acre in Nutcroft Furlong. With this acquisition, for which he was paying 15/- (75p) rent per half-year, he had the liberty to burn and carry away limestone. However, this was on the condition that by the following Michaelmas (1746) he had to build a substantial house of either brick or stone comprising two rooms up and two down.[2] This was, conceivably, the Finger Post Cottage once situated near the junction of the Wenlock–Sheinton road and demolished in the 1960s. Another house now stands on this site.

In January 1778 John Tomlins 'took' limerock in Homerfield (in the holding of Elizabeth Tomlins), limestone from which he had to pay the Wynnstay Estate 4d (1½p) per ton.[3] Because of the number of intervening years, this latter Tomlins may have been the son of William, hence the name Tomlinson's Hills.

Also in 1778 Thomas Cooper 'took' the Cave Leasow (situated in the north-east of Tomlinson's Hills, at map reference 625014) for the purpose of procuring limestone. His agreement also stated that he was to pay 4d (1½p) per ton and 'to get as deep as the rock will permit before removing fresh soil and to make good the land afterwards'. In addition, if lime could not be weighed, then royalties of 1/- (5p) had to be paid for each wagonload containing no more than 55 bushels and 8d (3p) for a cartload containing no more than 36 bushels.[4]

Only two years later, however, still at the Cave Leasow and adjoining lands, Sir Watkin Williams Wynn (of the Priory) leased limestone-bearing land for 21 years to the iron-making consortium of William Ferriday, William Goodwin and Thomas Botfield (probably trading as the Lightmoor Company). Payment was the same as for Tomlins and Cooper, but in the case of the consortium, a covenant was entered into requiring all fluxing stone to be used at the Lightmoor furnaces of the lessees or any other furnaces within ten miles 'except what is carried by John Brooke of Buildwas with six horses'. The stone was to be weighed publicly with three days' notice to be given in writing. Other conditions were: a) the limestone was not to be used for anything other than for lime or fluxing without consent; b) if the following were not complied with then Sir Watkin Williams Wynn succeeds; i) rent not being paid within 40 days of date due; ii) if no notice is given of weighing stone; iii) if no stone is extracted for six months; iv) if furnaces are stopped by accident for six months.[5] In the years 1789–90 the Lightmoor Company paid royalties on 1200 tons of limestone.[6]

This is the remains of a pot kiln adit at Tomlinson's hill built c. 1850.

By 1827 a tramway (or plateway) had been laid, as an extension from nearby Gleedon Quarry, to the River Severn at Buildwas.[7]

The limestone was then weighed (there is a cottage by the river still known as the 'weighhouse') before being loaded on to barges or trows for shipment downriver. This tramway had ceased to exist by 1848.[8]

In 1841 Edmund Mason (who was later to be found working Standhill Rock) had limestone interests somewhere in this vicinity, for which in the same year he paid Sir Watkin Williams Wynn £15 10s 0d (£15.50) in royalties.[9]

The year 1848 saw Tomlinson's Hills in the hands of Jonathan Aston, who may not have been winning limestone so much as using the site as grazing land.[10]

By 1879 the quarrier was Joseph Norry of Mardol Lane, now called Queen Street.[11] In fact Norry may have been at Tomlinson's Hills much earlier, for in 1871 the Wenlock Council ordered 'that a cart of lime be obtained from Joseph Norry and placed under the shed near to Mr Haynes's for purifying the main sewer'.[12]

According to the 2½-inch OS map of 1889 there was still quarrying taking place on Tomlinson's Hills, but also extensive disused workings.

It was around the end of the nineteenth century when the quarry finally closed. Norry was still the quarrymaster, but evidently financial constraints curtailed his quarrying career.[13]

Since Norry's occupation the quarry is now frequently referred to, especially by older residents of the town, as 'Norry's Hills'. Numerous

Members of the Royal Observer Corps on duty during the Second World War. This picture is not thought to be at Wenlock.

spoil heaps, small and shallow quarry faces and one or two pot kilns and adits can still be seen. Also, on the north-west periphery, a derelict Royal Observer Corps observation post is still standing. The northeast part of the quarry was partially filled in when in the 1950s, and until 1962, it was used as the town's refuse tip.[14] Near this refuse tip is the partially covered remains of what appears to have been a powder house.

References and Sources

1   S. Mullins, curator, Much Wenlock Museum, 1981
2   Wenlock Estate Book (Sir Watkin Williams Wynn), 1785
3   Wenlock Estate Book
4   Wenlock Estate Book
5   Wenlock Estate Book
6   Wynnstay box, National Library of Wales
7   R.F. Savage & L.D.W. Smith, 'Waggonways and Plateways of East Shropshire', thesis, Birmingham School of Architecture, 1965
8   1847 Tithe map
9   Wenlock Poor Rate Book, 12.5.1841
10 1847 Tithe map
11 *Kelly's Directory*, 1879
12 Wenlock Council Minute Book, 1871
13 B. Norry, grandson, 1968
14 Wenlock Council Minute Book, 3.5.1962

BOB'S ROCK QUARRY 630012 Very little is known about this unusually named quarry. But older residents have always referred to this quarry hole as Bob's Rock, suggesting that perhaps at some time a personage of that name quarried there.

The quarry did not exist on the 1847 Tithe map or on the Buildwas to Wenlock Railway Plan of 1855–9, but according to the six-inch OS map of 1889 it was designated as an old quarry, suggesting that it came into existence sometime around the period when the railway was laid from Buildwas, perhaps supplying stone for the construction of the railway. However, because of the original name of the site before it became a quarry (Bradley Piece) it could just conceivably have been an outlying source of limestone for the neighbouring Bradley Quarry or even Gleedon Quarry. The entrance appears to have been from the north-east with possibly a track to either quarry. Also, the track bed of the railway was laid virtually through the quarry, which may explain why extraction could have ceased prematurely.

What remains of Bob's Rock is an approximate six-metre-high face (with ballstone in evidence) overlooking about 1,000 square metres of quarry floor. There is no evidence of lime kilns being *in situ*.

Incidentally, the quarry floor, which was until very recently permanently waterlogged and thus tended to form a pool, provided a source of natural history and science (newts, tadpoles, frogs etc.) to generations of Wenlock children.

GLEEDON QUARRY 628015 This quarry was known originally as 'Glidton', then later as 'Glyddon', and after the Second World War as Farley Quarry.[1] Because of the mishmash of quarriers and quarrying agreements in this vicinity in the eighteenth century, it is possible that separate people and enterprises were working Gleedon, and even the north part of Tomlinson's Hills, in the same period.

The first evidence of quarrying was in 1728 when Thomas Owen was a 'lymeman' at Glidton. He died in the same year and his 'lyme and lyme tooles' were valued at £3 2s 6d (£3.12½). He was making a poor living (only just above the poverty line) with debts constituting a third of his estate.[2]

In 1767 the Coalbrookdale Company was probably quarrying at Gleedon (actually Buildwas is mentioned, but likely as not referring to the north and west part of Gleedon Hill) for fluxing stone for its Horsehay furnaces.[3]

In the years 1774–80 Joseph Hill and Company appeared to be the quarrier (but could have been producing limestone for the Coalbrookdale Company), in which time over 9,000 tons of fluxing stone was 'wagoned', at a cost of 2/6 (12½p) per cartload, from the river to the Horsehay blast furnaces.[4]

In March 1780 Sir Watkin Williams Wynn leased part of Gleedon Hill to Abraham and Samuel Darby, Richard Reynolds and Joseph Rathbone, all of the Coalbrookdale Company, for the procurement of lime, limestone and ballstone. Royalties were 4d (1½p) per ton (of 26 cwt per ton and each hundredweight containing 120 lb) and 1/- (5p) for every wagonload of lime. Other conditions were: a) only 1,500 tons per annum could be extracted, otherwise additional payments of 4d (1½p) would be required; b) if under 1,500 tons per annum was quarried, then the total amount over a two-year period could be made up to 3,000 tons; c) if the lessees did not burn into lime all waste and measure stone, then the lessor could, if convenient to the lessees; d) all stone was to be publicly weighed, and three days' notice had to be given in writing of weighing.[5]

The Coalbrookdale Company was still in possession of the north part of Gleedon in 1797, but after the turn of the century the Madeley Wood Company became the quarrymaster, by which time the area around Gleedon could have been known as Buildwas Limerocks.[6] Most of the limestone leaving the quarry at that time was destined for the Madeley Wood Company's furnaces at Ketley, Lightmoor and Horsehay.[7] At this time too, the Madeley Wood Company was renting part of the Coalbrookdale Company's Meadow Wharf at Coalbrookdale to unload limestone after shipment downriver from Buildwas and before cartage to its blast furnaces.[8]

After 1824 limestone was transported from the quarry to the river at Buildwas by a gravity tramway (or plateway), horses probably hauling the empty trucks back to the quarry.[9] This tramway, which extended south into Tomlinson's Hills, had ceased to exist by 1848.[10]

Thomas and William Botfield, the ironmasters of Old Park, Dawley, bought parts of Gleedon in 1810, 1826 and 1839.[11] Also in the 1830s Levi and Charles Tranter had quarrying interests somewhere on Gleedon Hill,[12] but like William James in 1838 they may have either been quarrying for the Botfields or renting part of their quarry.[13]

The Madeley Wood Company continued operations at Gleedon Quarry until 1849 (Reynolds and Anstice, on behalf of the Madeley Wood Company, were the lessees after 1824) when the company sold its limestone interests to James Foster, an ironmaster who had iron foundries around Broseley.[14] There is no record, however, of Foster ever quarrying at Gleedon. When the Madeley Wood Company ceased production, extraction was taking place at the most eastern point of the site, known then as Smalley Piece (some 18 acres or about seven hectares in extent) and near the present entrance to Farley Quarry.[15]

Also in the years 1848–51 Enoch Nickless was working a part of Gleedon Hill near and to the east of Sheinton Road.[16] This could have been for the owner, William Botfield. It was around this time that the latter was complaining about the cost of getting the limestone away from Gleedon.[17]

Around the middle of the nineteenth century Lord Forester had quarrying interests on the periphery of Gleedon. This was at Trapsrock, immediately east of Gleedon at map reference 630020.[18] Very little is known about the workings at Trapsrock, save that possibly Lord Forester could have been using the limestone on his estate.

Apart from a reference to Charles Sankey and Joseph Lloyd, the latter termed a farmer and 'stone dealer', in the years 1851–6[19] and an application by Lord Forester in 1861 to have rail sidings laid to the quarry (which did not come to fruition), Gleedon Quarry appears not to have been worked a great deal in the latter half of the nineteenth century. It was closed by 1901.[20]

In 1937 the construction firm Dudley Boswell temporarily reopened the quarry, at the Smalley Coppice end, for the extraction of building stone and hard core. Most of this material was used at the nearby Bradley Quarry, which at that time was being given a new lease of life as a petrol storage installation. The quarry was closed again by March 1938 when sufficient material had been won.

In 1947 the Lime Applications Ltd company (familiarly known as 'Lime Apps.') reopened Gleedon at map reference 630015 for the production of ground lime for soil fertiliser and for a small amount of limestone for burning into calcium oxide; because there were no lime kilns in a usable state remaining in the quarry, the latter operation took place at Shadwell Quarry.[22] A jaw crusher and a grinding mill

The derelict weighbridge at Farley Quarry in 1988.

An oil-fired lime dryer at Farley Quarry in 1960. Two storage hoppers are linked by the cylindrical drier. An elevator is visible to the left of the picture.

were installed, the latter being powered by a diesel engine mounted on a disused ex-army lorry.

The quarry had by that time become more familiarly known as Farley Quarry.

In 1953 Adam Lythcoe Ltd became the quarrier, Lime Applications Ltd having ceased trading and its assets sold off in the same year.[23]

In peak periods of spring and autumn in the mid fifties, Lythcoe's ground lime production was around 500 tons per week. The chief lime-spreading contractors at the time were the Irvine brothers. The senior brother, Tommy, was later to become a local director of Adam Lythcoe Ltd and manager of the quarry.[24] At the height of Lythcoe's production in the early 1960s, annual output of ground lime (virtually the sole product) was some 55,000 tons. In 1964 a more sophisticated hammer mill and drying plant were installed and about a dozen quarrymen were employed at the time who, in the busy spring and autumn periods, often had to work night shifts.[25]

Because of the substantial reduction in lime subsidy paid to farmers after 1965, trade fell away dramatically. With little fluxing or hard core trade to bolster sales, Adam Lythcoe ceased quarrying. This was just after the Town Council had received complaints about blasting operations and dust being emitted from the mills.[26]

The derelict Farley Quarry in 1988.

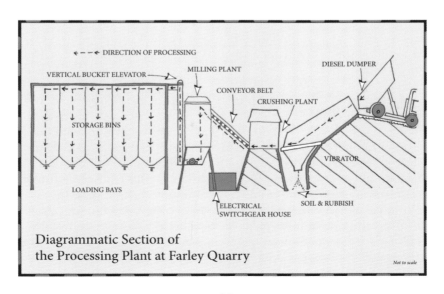

← – ← DIRECTION OF PROCESSING

VERTICAL BUCKET ELEVATOR

MILLING PLANT

DIESEL DUMPER

CONVEYOR BELT

CRUSHING PLANT

STORAGE BINS

VIBRATOR

LOADING BAYS

ELECTRICAL
SWITCHGEAR HOUSE

SOIL & RUBBISH

Diagrammatic Section of
the Processing Plant at Farley Quarry

Not to scale

The kiln adit at Farley Quarry had served three grates, or drawholes, and is seen here abandoned in 1960.

The quarry came back on stream in 1968 when the firm of Campbell & Jemson Ltd commenced operations. This firm concentrated predominantly on production of road stone and hard core, to which end upwards of 5,000 tons per week were sold in the early 1970s, together with some pulverised limestone for agricultural purposes. Campbell & Jemson ceased quarrying in 1983, due principally to the poor quality of limestone still available, even for hard core, whilst extraction of limestone for calcium carbonate had ceased even earlier.[27]

The quarry then lay dormant again until 1986 when the partnership of Huxley Brothers reopened the site for hard core production. However, this reopening was short-lived, because by 1988 the quarry was idle once more and the processing plant had been dismantled completely. With the dismantling of the lime storage hoppers, a kiln adit was exposed, which could date back to the Madeley Wood Company's occupation in the middle of the nineteenth century.

In 1991 a firm by the name of Donavan quarried in a small way using a mobile crushing plant. This firm's eventual aim was to convert the quarry into a refuse tip with a plastic skin lining the quarry floor to arrest any potential leakage of methane gas. This business appeared to have ceased trading by 1992. The site is completely derelict with the quarry floor resembling a moonscape.

References and Sources

1 Wenlock Borough guide book, 1955
2 S. Mullins, curator, Much Wenlock Museum, 1981
3 A. Raistrick, *Dynasty of Ironfounders* (London, Longmans, 1953)
4 Horsehay Company waste book, Stafford Records Office
5 Wenlock Estate Rent Book, 1785
6 B. Trinder, *The Industrial Revolution in Shropshire* (Chichester, Phillimore, 1973)
7 Trinder
8 Trinder
9 R.F. Savage & L.D.W. Smith, 'Waggonways & Plateways of East Shropshire', thesis, Birmingham School of Architecture, 1965
10 1847 Tithe map
11 1150/817, SRO
12 Wynnstay Estate Rent Book, 1838
13 Wynnstay
14 Trinder
15 1847 Tithe map
16 1847 Tithe map
17 K. Jones, railway historian, 1992
18 1847 Tithe map
19 Wenlock Rate Book, 1851, and *Post Office Directory*, 1856
20 D.C. Cox, *Victoria County History of Shropshire*, Vol. X
21 T.H. Thompson, scrapbook, Wenlock archives
22 J. Edwards, ex-quarryman, 1974
23 Wenlock Council Minute Book, 3.9.1953 & 4.12.1953
24 J. Moore, ex-quarryman, 1984
25 G. Brown, ex-foreman, Farley Quarry, 1973
26 Wenlock Council Minute Book, 3.6.1965 & 1.7.1965
27 T. Ridgeway, ex-fitter, Farley Quarry

BRADLEY QUARRY 634017 Early records of Bradley (pronounced Bradeley) date back to 1717 when Richard Reynolds of Coalbrookdale built a forge on the site of a paper mill in the vicinity of the quarry.[1] However, purely from the quarrying aspect, 1777 seems to be the date when Bradley became important for its limestone; in that year Richard Reynolds (of the Madeley Wood Company and a possible relative of the previously mentioned Reynolds) bought the lease of Bradley (and part of Whitwell) for £1,750 for the purpose of procuring limestone.[2]

According to an indenture dated 1827, Abraham Darby III, on behalf of the Coalbrookdale Company, had already acquired Bradley Rock and surrounding fields from Francis Pitt for £4,730.[3] And in the same year the quarry had become the sole source of fluxing for the company's Coalbrookdale and Lightmoor furnaces.[4]

As a direct result of limestone quarrying at Bradley and Gleedon at this time, Farley emerged as 'New Farley' with the largest occupation being 'road waggoners' hauling limestone to the river.[5] The hamlet then boasted three public houses, an infant school and a Methodist 'preaching station' and quarry owners were giving a gallon of beer as an inducement to work.[6]

In 1839 Murchison, the famous geologist, recorded that at Bradley 'copper pyrites and bitumen can be found in veins associated with white calcareous spar lining the interior cavities, joints, stratum and fissures.'[7] Could this, just conceivably, have been the locality which made Wenlock, in the reign of King Richard II, famous for its copper mines?[8]

Although in 1843 both the Anstice and Reynolds families seemed to have connections with Bradley Quarry,[9] possibly because of intertwining business interests between the Madeley Wood Company and the Coalbrookdale Company as well as through family ties, the latter concern was firmly in control in 1847, by which time the exposed area of the quarry was some four acres (about two hectares) in extent.[10]

In the years 1851–2 some 17,000 tons of Bradley lime and limestone was transported down the Farley road;[11] and by 1858 a weighing machine was *in situ*.[12] It was in this period too, that the Coalbrookdale Company must have been concerned with the cost and difficulty of transportation from Bradley because Abraham Darby commissioned A. & W. Jones, land surveyors of Broseley, to survey a tramway to its Meadow Wharf at Coalbrookdale. The routes proposed were: a) via Tickwood Hall; b) by skirting Tickwood Hall and then via (the now demolished) Burnt Houses; and c) via Vineyards Farm at Wyke and then by way of an inclined plane from the crest of Benthall Edge to the river below. The cost of these proposals varied between £1,949 and £2,341.[13] None of these schemes were implemented. No doubt the building of the standard gauge railway in 1862, with its connecting sidings to the quarry, resolved the problem. In fact an

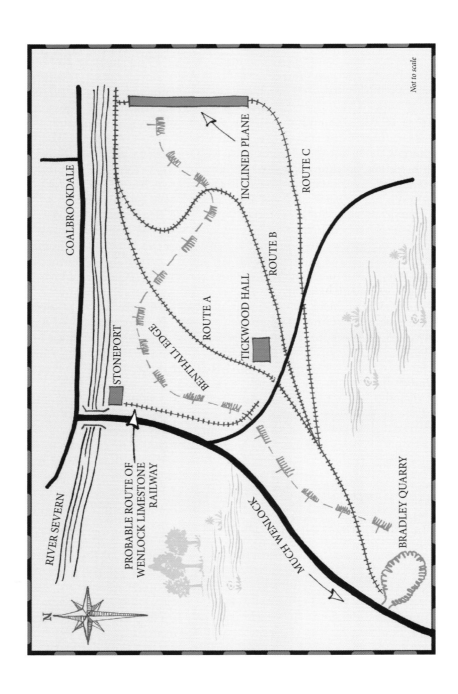

Much Wenlock's Limestone Quarries

124

application for sidings from the proposed railway was made as early as June 1860.[14] It was 1865, however, before fluxing stone could be sent direct by rail to the furnaces; this was because of the late opening of the Buildwas–Coalbrookdale spur.

By 1873 total output was 20,000 tons per annum with the fluxing production being virtually divided between the company's Dawley Castle and Lightmoor ironworks.[15]

In 1889 the Coalbrookdale Company ceased working Bradley, which, according to the 2½-inch OS map of the time, had become quite extensive. Four 15-ton-capacity kilns were in use plus stables, weighing machine, powder house and office buildings.[16] The lime kilns were situated near the rail sidings, the limestone being transported to them by means of an inclined plane from the workings above.[17]

Immediately after the Coalbrookdale Company discontinued quarrying at Bradley, Caleb Harper, a corn miller of Farley, became the new owner. Harper promptly leased the quarry to Adam Boulton, who was trading as A. Boulton & Company, Coal Merchants of Shrewsbury. This was still in 1889. The terms of the lease included a rent of £20 per annum (this was considerably less than rents being sought for limestone sites south-west of Wenlock at that time) plus royalties of 3d (1.25p) and 4d (2p) per ton for all stone and lime respectively sold. Another condition of the agreement was that the lessee should keep the quarry face perpendicular.[18]

By 1900 Boulton & Co. appeared to have shifted the emphasis to the production of lime, and especially cement, rather than limestone for fluxing or other uses. In fact the quarry then was called Bradley Lime and Cement Works and Boulton & Co. was advertising oven-made building, plastering and agricultural lime and best Portland cement.[19] By this time too, a row of new kilns, each of 40-tons capacity, had been built which may have been used for cement-making.[20] Forty to 50 men were employed at the time and their chief complaint was the effect of lime on their boot leather! [21]

A. Boulton & Company was the only concern to have manufactured cement in Wenlock quarries.

In 1901 the inclined plane claimed the life of a quarryman when he fell from an ascending truck under the corresponding descending one.[22]

In the 1914–18 war years quarry labour was supplemented by German prisoners of war.[23] It was in the war years too, in April 1917 in fact, that Robert Jones met his death through suffocation whilst working in the kilns.[24] The power for the quarry at this time was supplied by a stationary steam engine, the hooter of which could be heard in Wenlock; especially was this so on Armistice Day 1918, when it was sounded for a lengthy period as part of the celebrations.[25] The engine-man, from before the turn of the century to the quarry's closure, was Henry Longland.[26]

An old photograph of the Bradley Cement Works c. 1920.

Also in the First World War years, Boulton & Co. was supplying lime to the gasworks.[27]

After this period, which was to prove the twilight years as a limestone-producing site, quarrying became both difficult and costly, because of the extreme angle of the limestone beds descending under the overlying soil. This caused excessive thicknesses of overburden, which necessitated the employment of up to four men, with shovels and wheelbarrows, to remove – an expensive and time-consuming task.[28]

Adam Boulton & Company continued to work Bradley until its closure in 1932, which was probably due more to the economic climate appertaining at that time than to the inaccessibility of the limestone. From then until just prior to the Second World War, the buildings in the quarry and the steam engine were utilised as part of a creamery (Dingle Dairies) but were razed to the ground in 1938.[29]

For the whole of the period of Boulton & Company's occupancy of Bradley (43 years) the quarry foreman was Henry Hotchkiss.[30]

By the commencement of hostilities in 1939, the whole site had been taken over by the firm Trinidad Leaseholds, on behalf of the government, and a petrol storage installation was being built on it. The main contractor was Arup & Arup Ltd and it constructed 16 concrete tanks 25 feet (7.5 metres) underground with a 20-foot (6 metres) earth and rock topping. The total capacity was 12.5 million gallons of aviation spirit (to supply RAF airfields in the Midlands) and 0.7 million gallons of lubricating oil.[31]

The construction of these tanks claimed the lives of four workers in 1940 when they were electrocuted by contact with overhead power lines.[32]

After the completion of the storage facilities Bradley Quarry became known as 'The Petrol Dump' or simply 'The Dump'. And in the war years 'The Dump' boasted a small army camp, the soldiers from which formed a permanent guard.

The railway sidings to the quarry, which in latter years had been used for the railway oil tank wagons, were lifted at the same time as both the oil depot and the railway were closed in the early 1960s.

After the demise of Bradley as a major oil storage installation, Wenbridge Oil Co. Ltd became the new operator. This concern, however, used very little of the storage facilities.

A subsequent owner, Landowners Liquid Fertilizers Ltd, had the misfortune in 1993 to experience a fire and explosion in one of its small steel surface tanks, which killed one man and injured two others.

There is virtually no evidence now to suggest that Bradley was once a large and important quarry which made a significant contribution to the Industrial Revolution in east Shropshire.

References and Sources

1   M.B. Alderson, Coalbrookdale Archives Association
2   Cooper & Co. box, Shropshire Records Office
3   Cooper & Co. box
4   R.I. Murchison, *The Silurian System* (London, John Murray, 1839)
5   D.C. Cox, *Victoria County History of Shropshire*, Vol. X
6   T.H. Thompson, scrapbook, Wenlock Archives
7   Murchison
8   *Camden's Britannica*, 1722
9   Cooper & Co. box
10 1847 Tithe map
11 Summers/Adney/Brookes Railway Survey, 1852
12 Buildwas to Wenlock Railway Plan, 1858–9
13 Cooper & Co. box
14 Microfilm 113, Shrewsbury Local Studies Library
15 Microfilm 113
16 Lease, Bradley Quarry, 1889 (author)
17 2½-inch OS map, 1889
18 Lease, Bradley Quarry
19 *Kelly's Directory*, 1905
20 Thompson
21 Thompson
22 Thompson
23 G. Walters Snr, ex-quarryman, 1969
24 Coroner's Report, Wenlock Archives
25 Walters
26 Thompson
27 Wenlock Council Minute Book, 6.7.1916
28 T. Langford, ex-quarryman, 1965
29 Alderson
30 Thompson
31 Wenlock Council Minute Book, 3.11.1938
32 Thompson

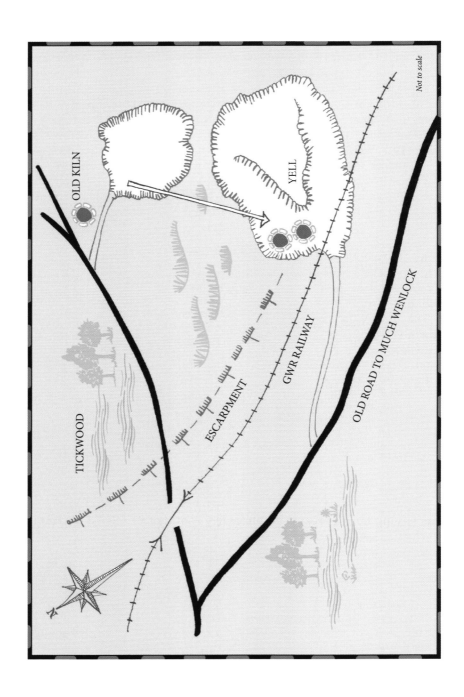

OLD KILN

YELL

Not to scale

TICKWOOD

ESCARPMENT

GWR RAILWAY

OLD ROAD TO MUCH WENLOCK

N

THE YELL or YELD QUARRY 637024 This quarry is situated in the Acklands (known originally as Hacklins) Coppice and limestone was being won from there as far back as 1714 when Richard Parsons was paying 10/- (50p) per annum rent for the lime kilns.[1]

Regrettably, no further references indicating limestone production from this vicinity occur for some considerable time. However, in 1803 Reynolds, Parry and Morris were transporting limestone from around this location on the 'Wenlock Limestone Railway' to just downstream from Buildwas bridge at 'Stoneport', from where it was shipped downriver.[2] In the period 1800–1 one barge alone made 21 voyages from the wharf with limestone whilst another made 14 voyages in the space of three months.[3]

In 1818 the partnership of Reynolds and Anstice (possibly on behalf of the Madeley Wood Company) sought to implement an agreement between themselves and Jesson and Davies (ironmasters) for the use of the railway to the River Severn. The users were to pay £100 for the right of way plus a levy of 2d (1.2p) per ton of limestone conveyed.[4] Whether any of these people were connected with the Yell Quarry it has not been possible to establish. However, with its nearness to 'Stoneport' and Coalbrookdale, it is just conceivable that they were.

The wharfage was still in use in 1832, when a bargeman was drowned whilst endeavouring to lift a large piece of limestone,[5] but the railway (probably a gravity 'plateway' with horses hauling the trucks back to the quarries) was defunct by 1833.[6]

In 1839 Murchison, the geologist, described the Yell as having an 80-foot (24 metre) ballstone face, superior limestone and in an accessible position.[7]

By 1847 Joseph Norry (perhaps the same person who later quarried at Tomlinson's Hills, but more likely an elder relative) was winning limestone from this site, the entrance to which was off the old Farley to Buildwas road (Shaw's Bank) at map ref. 636026.[8] Norry's lime production, however, was not great, only 30 tons in 1851 and none in the following year.[9] For the right to quarry at the Yell, Norry was paying Lord Forester a half-yearly rental of £1 13s 7d (£1.68) in 1853.[10] He had ceased working the quarry by 1858.[11]

It was Joseph Norry who gave the Yell, at that time, the alternative name of Norry's Rock.[12]

In 1859 Lord Forester applied for rail sidings to be laid into the quarry from the passing Buildwas–Wenlock railway.[13] This application, however, never came to fruition.

In 1889 the Yell seems still to have been working, but who the quarrymaster was it has not been possible to establish.[14]

It is probable that the quarry fell into disuse before the end of the nineteenth century. In fact, the railway from Buildwas to Wenlock was laid, on a high embankment (over which the present road now passes) right across the entrance to the quarry. If the Yell had been thought to have had sufficient and accessible reserves, then no doubt sidings, as applied for in 1859, would have been laid and loading wharves constructed, as had been done at most of the other quarries situated alongside the railway.

By 1902 the quarry had been abandoned.[15]

The Yell is now a heavily wooded and steep-sided area giving no indication, apart from one high face and the remnants of two pot kilns, that it was once a thriving quarry.

References and Sources

1   Manor of Wenlock Survey, 1714, National Library of Wales
2   B. Trinder, *The Industrial Revolution in Shropshire* (Chichester, Phillimore, 1973)
3   Trinder
4   Cooper & Co. box, Shropshire Records Office
5   Inquisition, 25.10.1832, Wenlock Archives
6   1-inch OS map, 1833
7   R.I. Murchison, *The Silurian System* (London, John Murray, 1839)
8   1847 Tithe map
9   Summers/Adney/Brookes Railway Survey, 1852
10 Lord Forester's Gathering Roll, 1853
11 Wenlock Council Rate Book, 1858
12 Buildwas–Wenlock railway map, Ironbridge Gorge Museum
13 Microfilm 113, Shrewsbury Local Studies Library
14 2½-inch Borough of Wenlock boundary map, 1889
15 6-inch OS map, 1902

WOODHOUSE QUARRY 639024 Much like its close neighbour, the Yell Quarry, little is known about the early days of the Woodhouse, although it is quite possible it did contribute to the traffic on the Wenlock limestone railway. Certainly Alexander Brodie, who worked the Calcutts ironworks at Jackfield in the 1780s, had limestone interests in this area,[1] as indeed did Joseph and Richard Jesson, the West Bromwich ironmasters, because in 1797 the latter (with partner Richard Wright) 'took a lease of stone under Wyke'.[2] But whether they quarried at this precise spot is a matter of speculation. Also in this area (Tickwood/Wyke) William Reynolds and partners took a lease of stone in 1800.[3]

The first positive evidence of quarrying at the Woodhouse was in 1847 when the Lawley Company was engaged in extracting limestone from this site.[4]

Much like some other quarries in the past, the Woodhouse appeared to have been worked by different people in the same years. For instance, Joseph Norry (who, it will be recalled, was also quarrying at the Yell) was at this location[5] at the same time as Francis Garbett was paying Lord Forester £30 per annum rent for the privilege of being there too![6] And in the years 1854–6 both the Anstice Company and William Cookson could be identified with the Woodhouse.[7] One qualification, however: there was a small farm in the vicinity called Woodhouse Farm, which may account for either or both Garbett and Cookson being there.

Woodhouse Quarry in 1900.

For how long the Anstice Company was interested in the Wood-house Quarry has been impossible to establish, but by 1878 Burnell and Son sought an explosive licence to blast rock at the Woodhouse.[8]

Just two years later Richard Onions was the quarrier and lime-burner.[9]

The quarry seems to have been working at the beginning of the twentieth century, but by then it appears to have lost its impor-tance, as the lime-burner then was James Reynolds, who was also the tenant of Woodhouse Farm.[10]

By 1902 the quarry had been abandoned.[11]

There can still be seen near the quarry face a pot kiln and adit.

A point of interest about this area (around the Woodhouse and Yell Quarries): in 1858 a local landowner (exactly who, it has not been possible to establish) employed a number of men in search of coal. Evidently several shafts were sunk at a considerable cost, but every spadeful brought to the surface contained only Silurian fossils.[12]

References and Sources

1   B. Trinder, *The Industrial Revolution in Shropshire* (Chichester, Phillimore, 1973)
2   Box 1224/58, Shropshire Records Office
3   D.C. Cox, *Victoria County History of Shropshire*, Vol. X
4   1847 Tithe map
5   Wenlock Rate Book, 1851
6   1851 Census
7   Wenlock Rate Books, 1854–6
8   Wenlock Council Minute Book, 4.2.1878
9   *Kelly's Directory*, 1880
10 *Kelly's Directory*, 1900
11 6-inch OS map, 1902
12 J. Randall, *Tourist's Guide to Wenlock* (Madeley, Lawley & Wenlock, Randall, 1875)

Conclusion and Acknowledgements

Limestone quarrying in the area ceased in 2007 and nobody in Much Wenlock today is involved in the local limestone industry, not that in direct proportion to the male working population of the town has quarrying (save for one or two isolated periods) ever been a major employer. That distinction, historically, must go to agriculture and possibly the service industries. For example, in the immediate post Second World War period over 40 male adults were working in the High Street alone and nine dairy herds were being milked in the town.

In the Preface mention was made that documentary evidence was scant and scattered. However, another source, less dispersed, was the knowledge and experience of local quarrymen. To these quarrymen then (some long since departed), who in the past 'worked in the rocks' and who so graciously gave of their time and knowledge to help me with these notes, I proffer my thanks.

I am also particularly grateful to the Wenlock archivists, the late Muriel Furbank and the late Glyn Macdonald. Without their help and co-operation it would not have been possible to expand and update these notes.

I also acknowledge my indebtedness to various authors from whose works I have gleaned technical information; to quarry owners ECC and Steetley and other individuals for permission to use certain photographs and the Avery Company for its illustration of a weighbridge.

The last remaining tramway.

Wenlock limestone was used in the construction of this now vanished
railway bridge.

The state of the quarries October 2014.

Key to Quarry Locations

1   Hilltop
2   Lilleshall
3   Plough
4   Knowle
5   Westwood
6   Lea
7   Wenlock
8   Coates
9   Cuckoo's Nest
10 Kiln Leasows
11 Ballstone
12 Meakin's
13 Trowe's
14 Harp
15 Stokes Barn Bank
16 Edgefield
17 Smokey Hole
18 Gallows Tree Leasows
19 Demesnes
20 Willmoor Hill
21 Sytche
22 Standhill
23 Shadwell
24 Tomlinson's Hills
25 Bob's Rock
26 Gleedon
27 Bradley
28 Yell
29 Woodhouse